How to help your
ALCOHOLIC

Stan West

How to help your alcoholic

Second edition:

March 2019

Contents

Dear Reader

If you have picked up this book then you probably have a spouse, partner, loved-one or close friend whose drinking is causing you concern. The purpose of this book is to explain how the mind of an alcoholic works and show you what you can do to help them.

The single most important thing to understand about an alcoholic is that they are mentally ill: alcoholism is an illness, not a moral weakness. Alcoholism is an addiction, but unlike other addictions; heroin, cannabis, or gambling for example, alcoholism is so common that it has its own name; it is addiction nonetheless.

The human brain is an incredibly complex thing. It has evolved through the eons to be the pinnacle of self-learning and problem solving on the planet. Our brains have evolved to make us more successful at surviving adversity than any other species, and have many pre-defined instinctive processes to help us achieve this. In alcoholics some of these processes have become unhelpfully associated with the acquisition and consumption of alcohol. Their minds have established subconscious processes which constantly search for alcohol and the means to acquire it. Alcoholics haven't chosen this. It is done without their awareness or approval, and they do not even know it is happening.

Addiction is a corruption of mental processes where the addict recognises the benefit of continued use of some substance or activity but not the harm that it causes; they see the benefits but are blind to, and will deny the damage. Alcoholics perceive alcohol as bringing happiness and relief from distress, and they see it as the only available relief from their distress. They cannot see it as a problem itself, and they cannot see that much of the distress they suffer is caused by the very thing that they think is helping them.

Addiction is a mental feedback loop. Alcoholics drink to be happy. They do (or don't do) things while drunk that cause distress. They accumulate guilt and shame. Drinking relieves this distress briefly. Their minds learn that distress is relieved by drinking and engage an ancient and primitive seek/reward mechanism that impels them to find alcohol again every time they are distressed. On acquiring drink they are rewarded with a wonderful surge of dopamine though their brains. Dopamine is a drug the brain releases to produce the sensation of relaxation and joy. But when they sober up they quickly return to their distressed state; nothing has happened to change that, so they seek drink again. Once established this is a completely automated looping process that they have no influence over whatsoever, and they are blinded to the fact that they are locked into a downward spiral... the deeper they go, the more urgent the demand that they find drink. The compulsion to drink has no words, shape or form. It is a deep, instinctive and powerful feeling that is as urgent as needing to breathe, or flee from danger.

The only way out of this downward trajectory is to stop drinking completely, but this is an unimaginable thought to an alcoholic. Over time their memories have become distorted to present drinking as being fun... ultimately it is the only source of happiness they can recall. They cannot imagine life being worthwhile without alcohol; it means a life without fun. So why would they want to stop? This is the extent of their entrapment.

The alcoholic's fight is not with the bottle, but with their own mind. Their foe is themselves. It is therefore precisely as cunning and deceptive as they can be, except that they also have to fight primal survival drives with nothing but intellect and willpower. On a good day they are only equal to their addiction, on a bad day they will succumb to its demands. It is not a fair fight. The scales are tipped against them and they need help if they are going to win through.

You haven't caused anyone to become alcoholic, and you can't stop them either. As much as you may wish it you can't make them well again, they are the only ones that can do that. You can help them, but you are not responsible for their recovery; they are. "You can lead a horse to water, but you can't make it drink".

Their fight is huge, and the scales are not tipped in their favour. They need guidance, strength and support from people whose minds are not distorted by the damage caused by addiction. They need reminding of when their minds are lying to them, they need reassurance when the peaks of withdrawal have them begging for relief, and they need affirmation that life without alcohol is both possible and worthwhile.

The bad news is that un-checked alcoholics die before their time: from organ failure, traumatic accidents (car crashes etc.) or suicide.

The good news is that most alcoholics do recover, and that you can help them.

Alcoholic!

A diabetic is someone who suffers from diabetes. If someone refers to a sufferer as a diabetic then it is said with implied compassion. This is not the case for an alcoholic. An alcoholic is someone who is afflicted by alcoholism, but that word is rarely accompanied by compassion, it is usually said with implied disgust. If someone is addicted to tobacco then people blame tobacco and the tobacco companies, but if someone is addicted to alcohol they blame the person.

Society generally portrays alcoholism as a shameful state that the sufferer has brought on themselves. An alcoholic is generally regarded as someone contemptible; they are weak and should exercise more control, they are beyond help, their problems are of their own making and they do not warrant sympathy.

But this overlooks a fundamental of addiction. The general view of society is that alcoholics simply need to grow a backbone and exercise some control over themselves. But that control isn't available to the sufferer. Alcoholics do not make poor choices regarding drinking; they have no choice to make. They don't choose to drink, they have to drink.

A normal drinker can choose whether or not to drink, and can choose when they've had enough. If they drink too much when they should have stopped then they don't expect sympathy;

they have brought this on themselves by not exercising better control. They apply the same standard to alcoholics, but an alcoholic has no such freedom of choice. In them it is absent, and in its place is a wordless, primal, urgent and instinctive demand that they find drink, and find it now. Once drinking then there is no thought coming from the back of their mind saying "that's enough now", instead there is always the opposite.... "There's time for one more!"

Alcoholism is not poor behaviour, but corrupted mental processes. It is not moral weakness, but a reversal of the normal checks and balances that accompany drinking, whereby "I shouldn't drink now" has been replaced by "I should".

Alcoholism

There is no single point at which someone becomes alcoholic, and it is not determined by how much they drink. In fact alcoholism has remarkably little to do with alcohol at all. There is another drug, that our brain produces naturally, which is central to the formation of addiction.

Dopamine is involved in many aspects of our brain's functions. It motivates us to take action toward certain goals, desires, and needs, and gives us a surge of reinforcing pleasure when we achieve them. Serotonin is another of the brain's "feel-good" drugs. When it is present it gives us the feeling of being socially significant or important. The starting point for the addiction process is that dopamine induces pleasure. When dopamine is released into our brain it is detected by "receptors", and in one particular part of the brain these receptors induce the sensation of pleasure when they are activated.

However alcohol mimics the very chemical that triggers the release of dopamine and serotonin. Alcohol fools the brain into thinking that it should release both dopamine and serotonin, and this (among other things) triggers the sensation of happiness and of being somebody significant. This is why we like alcohol; it makes us feel good and it makes us feel good among other people. But dopamine is not only responsible for making us feel good, it has other important functions.

The human brain is an incredible organ. It is massively capable, self-teaching, and self-improving. It is constantly doing far more than we are aware of, and while we may feel that we are in conscious control of what we are doing at any time, in fact much of what we do is conducted without conscious effort or even our awareness. Also, the brain constantly seeks to improve its own efficiency. Things that at first require huge concentration to achieve, like riding a bicycle for example, become effortless with practice and repetition. If we repeat tasks often enough they become so optimised in the brain that they require no conscious effort at all; they happen automatically. This self-learning and self-improving capacity allows us to do complex things without the need for conscious involvement, and it is one of the key components of addiction.

Our brains are self-learning as well as self-improving, but they are not entirely blank canvasses when we are born; there are some pre-defined processes that guide and direct us. These processes evolved over millions of years, and are not exclusive to humans; they are also present in most animals. They are pre-defined procedures that aid survival and two are particularly important in relation to addiction: things that are discovered to be dangerous or harmful are remembered and deterred, whereas things that are beneficial are remembered and encouraged. Things that we should not repeat are discouraged by invoking fear or disgust in us, while things that should be done again are encouraged by invoking delight and pleasure. As we progress through life we accumulate more and more of these "encourage" or "avoid" examples, and a new process is established for each.

On encountering something new we examine it to see if it is good, bad, or benign; this is a conscious process and is initiated by our natural inquisitiveness. If something is found to be good then it is remembered as warranting encouragement, if something is bad then it is remembered as something to be deterred. These systems are highly evolved. Berries for example are to be sought out; they contain sugars and vitamins that are important to survival, but some berries are poisonous. Berries generally are identified as to be sought out, but some poisonous ones are to be avoided. To each of these there is an importance assigned to the activity. While berries can be nutritious the poisonous ones can be fatal. The "avoid" activity gets a far higher importance than the "encourage" activity. In our brains the "avoid" process prevails over the "encourage"; eating berries is good, but eating poisonous berries is not.

Once established these processes cease to be conscious and inquisitive thought processes, they become learned, remembered, and entirely automatic. They bypass our conscious minds. If we have identified something as beneficial or harmful then the next time we encounter it our brain proceeds directly to invoking a reward sensation or disincentive sensation without including any conscious thought process. But the brain does more than simply reward us for finding something beneficial; it actively searches for things on the "beneficial" list, and motivates us to actively seek them out.

Not only do our minds continuously search for things on the beneficial list, but when signs of their presence are detected then we are alerted to being near them and motivated to acquire them *now*. Evolution has made the brain impart urgency to the acquisition of beneficial things. Something of value that is available now might not be found again for some time, so our brains encourage us to take advantage of the opportunity while it is present. We experience this motivation as a craving.

This function was famously described in an experiment known as the "marshmallow test". A group of children was put into a room and in front of each of them was placed a marshmallow. The facilitator told them he had to go away for a few minutes. The children could eat the marshmallow or wait a few minutes until he got back, when they could have two.

Half the children could not wait a few minutes and took the single marshmallow over the greater reward they would get if they only waited a while. Addicts are among that half; people whose disposition is to take the smaller reward now rather than the greater reward later.

Not only do we experience our attention being drawn to the availability of something beneficial, if it is close then its perceived value also increases dramatically, and we are motivated to acquire it more urgently. The process demonstrated in the marshmallow test is known as "delay discounting": we will choose a benefit that is close to us over a significantly greater benefit that lies a little in the future or a little further away. Additionally, these functions that seek and then motivate us to acquire certain things are not only activated through our senses, they are also triggered by our imagination. The "seek" and "encourage" processes cannot distinguish between what is real, and what is imagined. To these processes everything appears real, so if we daydream about something on the desirable list, like strawberries and cream for example, then the seek process thinks that they are close, and creates a craving to encourage us to secure some. Urgency is increased when we are near to (or imagine) something that has been identified as beneficial, and dopamine is released into our brains when we secure it.

This is where we start to link addiction to our normal brain functions. When dopamine is released it gets detected in various parts of the brain. In one part it invokes pleasure as a strong sensation of ease and comfort. However, in another part of the brain, the "remember this, it is a good thing to repeat" process is also triggered. Dopamine is not only responsible for inducing pleasure, but also for causing the pleasure creating item or activity to be remembered. The part of the brain that stores this is different to our regular memory. Our main memory simply records facts, details and events, but this part of memory remembers the detail with an associated emotion and a value of its importance.

When we drink alcohol the brain is fooled into releasing dopamine, and this triggers the mechanism that gives us the strong sensation of joy and wellbeing. But it also adds alcohol to the remembered list of things that are beneficial and to be sought out. What we remember is: "drink = happy, important".

Alcohol fools the brain into thinking that dopamine *should* be released, and this is how the alcohol trap forms. We drink alcohol, we enjoy it, we remember that alcohol is a good thing, and we set in place the process that motivates us to actively seek it out. We have no awareness whatsoever that this has taken place, and once activated this mechanism constantly and silently encourages us to seek and consume alcohol.

The onset of addiction

The dopamine "reward system" as it is called is the starting point of addiction, but not everybody who drinks alcohol (or takes another addictive drug) becomes addicted; there are other related processes in play.

If we stand on a hilltop where we can see a long way, and we look over a large lake or sea, then we get a strong sense of wellbeing; this is a dopamine surge. Dopamine has been released for three reasons:-

- We are close to plenty of water (vital to our survival)
- We are above our surroundings (therefore safer from predators)
- We can see a long way (also, safer from predators)

There are three independent things that have invoked the reward mechanism; we have done some things that are beneficial to our survival. However, if that same hilltop we were stood on was a cliff edge, then the opposite mechanism, the deterrent system is triggered:- danger! and fear is induced to make us move away.

In most people alcohol is listed in both the reward system and the deterrent system. Alcohol consumption has an "avoid!" mechanism attached to drinking too much, or drinking at the wrong time. Normal drinkers have deterrent processes linked to the consequences of drinking too much: i.e. memories of hangovers, vomiting and loss of control, and these deterrent processes also link to failing to meet other important obligations if they drink. But for some reason this mechanism does not activate strongly in alcoholics.

The consensus among scientists is that addiction is caused by altered learning systems that overvalue pleasure and undervalue risk in relation to alcohol. Addicts also fall into the group that fail the Marshmallow Test; they favour immediate reward ahead of greater benefits later. These are the three characteristics that make someone susceptible to addiction. In one sense the likelihood that addiction will take hold is partially genetic. A parent having these three characteristics is more likely to pass them on to the next generation than a parent that does not. But that is not a certainty, and being vulnerable to addiction doesn't mean that someone *will* become addicted. To become addicted requires both the pre-disposition *and* repeated engagement in an addictive activity.

With repeated alcohol use, the dopamine reward system assigns increasing value to perceived benefit of drinking. When something is very highly valued then the motivation to acquire it (the craving) gets bigger and dopamine surge released on securing it is also bigger. Alcoholics experience a very significant sensation of feeling good on acquiring alcohol, and the memory is further reinforced that this was a good thing. The brain learns through repetition and the alcohol-seeking mechanism strengthens, gets faster and becomes preferred above other alternatives. But unlike in the brains of normal drinkers there is no formation of a deterring memory when alcohol leads to a bad outcome. Omitting to record the bad experience incorrectly undervalues the risk and leads to repeating previous mistakes. For its addicts alcohol steals the joy, meaning and purpose from life while simultaneously offering an empty promise of fun.

These combined characteristics favour addiction; and not just to alcohol, but addiction in general. One study showed that alcoholism is 10 times more common among smokers than among non-smokers, and the factors that favour addiction also dis-favour being able to break its grip. Non-alcoholic smokers are seven times more likely to be successful in their attempt to stop smoking than alcoholic smokers.

The inability to properly recognise the adverse consequences of drinking is perfectly apparent. Alcoholics drink with complete disregard to the fact that a severe hangover will follow; they are not prompted that this will happen and should be avoided. They will also drink at inappropriate times; like before important meetings, at work, or on occasions where sobriety is expected, again, because they receive no mental prompt to do otherwise.

In alcoholics the urge to seek out alcohol is very firmly established, and the impulse to avoid it is barely, if at all present. So the alcoholic always finds it appropriate to drink, and is never presented with a repulse from it. Even while heavily hungover an alcoholic will still want to drink again once the alcohol level in their bloodstream ceases to stimulate dopamine release, and they will drink in ways that are completely contradictory to their own standards of sensible behaviour.

For example, an alcoholic will drink before driving and picking up children. They know this is an extremely bad, dangerous and foolish thing to do; they would condemn this behaviour in others. But in the time that preceded picking up the children their mind presented no objection to drinking; in fact the opposite happened. Their mind encouraged them to seek out and secure drink. It rewarded them for finding drink, and once they had begun drinking their brain never said "stop!" but instead insisted "there's time for one more".

These are the mechanisms by which the addiction feedback loop is established, and exactly like learning to ride a bike, every time this loop is traversed the neural pathway becomes firmer and faster. The mental processes being reinforced are not apparent to the sufferer. They operate without their awareness or permission, and are automatic, involuntary and obligatory.

The alcoholic is aware of none of the changes in their brain in relation to finding and consuming alcohol; to them everything about their drinking seems normal... everything that is except the way that others are starting to talk about it. As their addiction deepens the alcoholic perceives the problem to be "in the eye of the beholder" and not in themselves, and this is the truth for them; they genuinely perceive no problem. The onlooker watching someone become steadily more and more regularly drunk sees a problem, but the alcoholic sees none. This is due to the different perceptions. The onlooker is seeing the alcoholic from an un-tainted viewpoint; their thought processes associated with alcohol are not distorted. To them too much alcohol is bad.

To the alcoholic, alcohol is good, and more alcohol is also good... and they are confused as to why other people don't see it that way.

Chronic, fatal and progressive

Alcoholism is a chronic illness that is progressive, and if unchecked, fatal.

"Chronic" is used here in the medical sense. Chronic does not mean that an illness is severe, it means it is forever. Chronic illnesses are those that are long lived; the sufferer usually has them for the rest of their life. This is the case for alcoholism; it can be treated, but it can't be cured. Alcoholism can't be cured because of its origins in the mind. Once the mental connections have been made that make alcohol something to be sought out, and also something not to be avoided, then these are locked in place for life. This is a fundamental feature of the brain. Once we have learned something, then it can't be unlearned. Relief from alcoholism therefore requires that, while we can't remove these unwanted connections, we must stop using them in favour of others. This is incredibly difficult, both to achieve and to sustain. While we may over time develop alternate routes through our minds, the old pathways are still present, and can be re-traversed at any time. This is why relapse is so common.

Left completely unchecked alcoholics will drink themselves to death; the primal force that insists that they drink is incredibly powerful and insatiable. However, alcoholism is rarely completely unchecked; the sufferer may lack the means to acquire as much alcohol as they need, they get hospitalised and de-toxified, they are committed into treatment, or they die either accidentally or deliberately. With medical treatment becoming more available and more effective the most likely cause of death for an untreated alcoholic is either accident or suicide.

Alcohol itself does not make people suicidal; rather it contributes to a mounting burden of shame, guilt and worthlessness. As addiction deepens many alcoholics find that life is so unbearable that it is better to die than to continue living. This is an inevitable conclusion of the illness's progression if it is left to run amok.

The body is affected by regular and large doses of alcohol in very many ways. The gastric system, liver and kidneys are all damaged through prolonged contact with alcohol. But these problems can mostly be remedied by medical intervention. It is the way the brain changes that is the most problematic.

The brain is not like other organs in the body. The other organs develop to maturity and then remain like that for the remainder of our lives. But the brain is constantly changing; learning and adapting in response to our changing situations.

The brain changes to maintain and improve its own performance. The first adaptation to prolonged exposure to alcohol is that tolerance increases. Alcohol is defined as a "depressant". This does not mean it makes people depressed, it means that it slows down the speed of mental processing. Everyone experiences the effect of this if they become intoxicated: the speed of the brain slows down so that difficult and complex tasks can no longer be performed quickly enough for them to be conducted successfully. For example, walking upright is a learned skill. It requires the simultaneous coordination of all the large muscles in our body in response to information coming from our ears and eyes. It takes months to learn how to stand and walk, and only through repeated practice does it become sufficiently learned that we can do it fast enough to move without staggering. When we drink a lot of alcohol our brain function slows, and we can no longer coordinate all the muscle movements quickly enough to move smoothly or even stay upright.

The brain responds to this impediment to its function by releasing stimulants to temporarily speed up processing. If the brain is regularly exposed to high levels of alcohol then its ability to create the stimulant increases, in exactly the same way that regular exercise increases muscle size. As the brain produces more stimulant to counter the slowing effect of alcohol then a heavy drinker can consume far more alcohol before their mental function is seriously impaired. Prolonged heavy drinking leads to increased alcohol tolerance. But that increased stimulant production has additional effects which lock addiction in place even more firmly.

If the sufferer is drinking daily, and in significant amounts, then there is a constant presence of stimulant. This means that while not drinking the alcoholic experiences a racing mind, jumpiness and irritability. This racing mind will not slow enough to allow sleep; it will keep them awake at night, and the only way they know to offset this is to drink before going to bed.

The second physical change that occurs in the brain relates to the production of dopamine. Dopamine causes the wave of ease and contentment an alcoholic feels when they take their first drink. It is dopamine that causes this sensation, not alcohol. Dopamine is released into the brain in response to securing alcohol and then by the presence of alcohol. The elated sensation occurs before the alcohol is even absorbed into the bloodstream. For as long as the person keeps drinking the alcohol in their blood fools the brain into thinking that more dopamine and serotonin should be released. With regular and repeated heavy drinking the brain recognises it is releasing more dopamine than intended. It recognises there is too much dopamine and in response it reduces the number of cells actively producing it and detecting it.

The same reduction happens to serotonin production. While the alcoholic is drinking then their brain is fooled into releasing serotonin, and accordingly they become socially confident. But when the normal background level of serotonin reduces then they experience loneliness and social insecurity when not drinking.

The lowering of the regular dopamine level also has a profound effect on the heavy drinker; their overall daily sensation of pleasure is lowered, and they are unhappy when not drinking. The simplest relief from this discontent is to take a drink. They will get the immediate wave of ease and comfort when they take the first drink, but now they now need to drink more to feel good.

The effects of reduction in the regular dopamine and serotonin levels and the constant presence of stimulant combine. When the alcoholic is not drinking they are agitated, lonely and depressed. The only way to regularise the brain now is to have a drink.

When the addiction has reached this point of development then the sufferer has to drink simply to feel normal; they have to drink to achieve the same sense of personal comfort that they had before ever drinking at all. Once a heavy drinker has begun to drink to relieve this discomfort then the downward spiral is firmly locked into place. They drink to get relief from the misery of the lower dopamine levels, they drink to get rid of the racing mind and irritability, and they have to drink far more to gain any sense of pleasure from drinking. Drinking more further reduces the number of cells producing and detecting dopamine and serotonin thus making them lonelier and more miserable... so they drink.

Alcoholics drink in response to entirely automated processes that they are completely unaware of and every time they repeat the cycle the brain learns more deeply and the processes become faster and more dominant. Over an extended period of time the first and immediate response to feeling any distress is to have a drink. Others are added too; tired? → drink, lonely? →drink, angry? → drink, hungry? → drink.

By this stage the alcoholic is drinking completely compulsively. Their normal state is that their minds are racing and they feel unhappy, isolated and irritable. They now need to drink what most people would consider an excessive amount just to feel normal. They can now no longer drink enough to become happy; they pass out first. But as soon as they wake the demand to drink again will be there.

As more and more of their time gets committed to drinking, and to being functionally impaired as a result of drinking, their place in the world starts sliding backwards. They start failing to meet the standards society expects, as well as their own, and they start failing at work and at home. Their standing in the world is in decline and the damage to their self-image is huge. They begin to sense that they are failures and despite their efforts they feel unrecognised and unvalued. Ultimately they start to feel completely worthless, and life itself: pointless.

They have vaguely linked drinking as a part of this demise in their social standing, but it is by now only one of very many issues troubling them; they are surrounded by problems... their life is nothing but problems, and they can see no escape from this misery. By this time they will have tried to control their drinking many times. There will have been numerous occasions where they intended to not drink, or only have a couple, but the silent demand to drink overwhelmed them.

It is difficult to describe this wordless compulsion to those who have not experienced it, but this is similar:

Imagine you are in a room. There is no-one else there except a baby, and the baby is crying. The crying nags terribly. You only have to pick the baby up to stop it crying, but you're not allowed to. It carries on crying. The longer you leave it alone the more insistent the crying becomes. Even though it would be very easy to pick up the baby and make the screaming stop, you mustn't. You can't get away from the screaming, and it just goes on, and on and on; it never stops. Time passes very slowly, and the crying continues, and continues without pause. It is impossibly irritating. Eventually it becomes too much, and you yield. You pick up the baby.

That's what it's like when an alcoholic doesn't drink for a while. The demand that you pick up the baby feels precisely like the demand that an alcoholic pick up a drink. It has no words, shape or form; it is just an urgent imperative demand. The longer they resist, the more urgent the demand becomes, until eventually they have to give in to it.

There is no sudden dividing line at which somebody either is or isn't an alcoholic. Alcoholism is progressive and develops very slowly. It creeps on so slowly that the sufferer is completely unaware of the changes in them. Also, because it is a progressive illness not all alcoholics experience or exhibit the same severity of symptoms; some are sicker than others. But in general terms the longer they have been drinking heavily the more entrenched is their addiction. But they won't really be aware of it. They will only be able to recognise a long tem trend of a gradual increase in the amount they drink.

These are some of the behaviours alcoholics display as their addiction strengthens.

- Drinking before a drinking function
- Repeating unwanted drinking patterns
- Drinking at inappropriate times
- Morning shakes or tremors
- Lying about how much they drink, when and where
- Not wanting to talk about their drinking
- Wanting to continue drinking when it's time to leave
- Missing work or family obligations
- Hiding alcohol
- Setting drinking limits and not being able to stick to them
- Behaving out of character when drinking
- Eating becomes less important than drinking
- Surrounding themselves with heavy drinkers
- Drinking early in the morning
- Engaging in risky sexual behaviour when drunk

- Being irritable, nervous or uncomfortable when not drinking
- Regular occurrence of memory loss or blackouts
- Attempted periods of abstinence
- Personal relationships become less important than drinking
- Thinking becomes scattered and impaired
- Exhibiting some or all of these symptoms isn't the measure of whether or not someone is an alcoholic. The key measure of this is whether or not they are able to stop drinking when they choose to; and only the sufferer will know this with absolute certainty. In fact they are the only person that needs to know that this is true, but they are often the last to think it.
- While some progression into alcoholism is observable, much more is kept hidden. The sufferer recoils from the shame associated with the word "alcoholic!" and covers their tracks to conceal the true extent of their drinking. In the face of mounting distress and depression they carry on pretending that nothing is wrong, but deep inside they feel that everything is wrong. While there is a progression of indicators visible to the observer, there is another progression, things that the sufferer is aware of but conceals from public display.

- Sneaking drinks or minimizing how much they actually consume
- Increasing alcohol tolerance
- Getting anxious when people are talking about those who drink too much
- Drinking to relieve uncomfortable emotion and stress
- Uncomfortable in a situation where there is no alcohol
- Using alcohol as a reward
- Inability to control alcohol intake after starting to drink
- Needing the first drink of the day
- Waking thoughts are preoccupied with drinking
- Feelings of real guilt about drinking
- Developing unreasonable feelings of resentment towards other people and the world
- Thinking of getting away as way to stop drinking
- Routinely drinking alone (hiding their drinking from public sight)
- Guilt extends into constant remorse
- Obsessing about alcohol (i.e. the next time they can drink, how they are going to get alcohol, who they're going to drink with)
- Lost moral compass −(start doing things they wouldn't have considered previously)
- Angry when their drinking is discussed

- Increasing sense of denial that their heavy drinking is a problem
- Experiencing fear that is not attached to any apparent threat
- Not being able to imagine their life without alcohol in it
- Desperately alone, restless, irritable, confused, depressed and scared
- Extremely low self-esteem. Nothing they try to do improves things
- Sense of complete hopelessness and impending doom
- Suicidal thoughts and planning

At the same time as they are aware that their position is untenable their mental state is increasingly perilous. Deep down they know that something is wrong with their drinking, but they have other stresses too. Every aspect of their lives is unravelling, and in addition to that there is a mounting burden of guilt. They drink secretly; hiding from the sight of others. That's the only way they can drink as much as they need without being shamed. They do things that offend their own consciences time after time, and the list of their inappropriate behaviours is beyond counting; things they would never normally do, but things they've done nonetheless. They are completely confused as to how they've reached this point and the massive burden of guilt and shame keeps increasing.

They now can't stop thinking about their troubles unless they have a drink. Their brains are so conditioned to the presence of alcohol that there is a massive oversupply of stimulant to keep the brain functioning. When they are not drinking their mind is a roaring and tumbling torrent of unresolved issues, bad outcomes, and guilty secrets. They play and re-play scenes in their mind to try to find different resolutions but they will not come, so the issues spin and twist and churn relentlessly.

They feel impossibly alone and scared; scared that their secrets will be found out and scared that this is it... this is all their life has amounted to. The loneliness is crushing. Even though they are surrounded by people, at home and at work, no-one seems to recognise how hard their life has become. No-one understands, and no-one is coming to help; they are on their own.

Alcohol is the only thing that gives them relief. It is the only thing that makes life bearable. They are impossibly trapped, and can see no way out. They can't control or limit their drinking; they've tried this many times and failed completely. They've tried to stop for periods, but usually only managed a few days... it's impossible. Their position is hopeless; they are without hope. A life without alcohol is utterly unimaginable.

They can't stop drinking, but they can't carry on either.

To this point in the book we've looked at alcoholism; how it forms, the instinctive processes involved, how it progresses, and how the alcoholic experiences it. These are presented in general terms as these things are broadly consistent across all alcoholics and addicts.

If you have picked up this book then it is not because your concern is broad and general, it is because you have a spouse, partner, loved-one or close friend that you are worried about. From this point on we look, not in general, but at what you can do to help that person in particular. To avoid constant repetition of the phrase "spouse, partner, loved-one or close friend" this person is given a name: Lee.

Lee

In the preceding chapters we have looked generally at alcoholism and alcoholics and we looked at the illness's progression. If you recognise sequences of these progression steps in Lee then they are in severe trouble, but they probably won't recognise or acknowledge it themselves. Right now you probably know more about their condition than Lee does.

If you are trying to help someone with a serious drinking problem then you have a major barrier to remove before any progress is possible, and that barrier is denial. Denial that alcohol is a problem for them isn't just a common trait among alcoholics; it is present in every single case. It isn't just a feature to be aware of; it is one of the listed symptoms.

Denial

If Lee's addiction has become problematic then they already have a wide range of mental defence mechanisms working away to protect their alcohol supply. The mind craves alcohol, and moves to assure its continued availability. Again, this is a subconscious process. Lee isn't being selfish or stubborn; they genuinely perceive no problem with continued drinking. As far as they can see it is a good thing, not a bad thing. This is a genuinely held belief. Or if they acknowledge that drinking causes some problems then they will have apparently rational defences for them.

"Cognitive dissonance" is the mental discomfort felt by simultaneously holding two ideas that contradict each other. The brain likes things to be orderly and resolved, and two conflicting ideas can be dangerous; e.g. do you run from a snake, or do you stay still. When conflicting ideas exist we are given a feeling of distress to draw our attention to them. This is done so that we concentrate on them in order to resolve the conflict, and dismiss either one idea or the other. With regard to alcohol the conflict is "drinking is good" vs "drinking is bad".

It is cognitive dissonance that stops most people that drink from becoming alcoholics. The distress caused by cognitive dissonance encourages us to choose either one or the other of the conflicting ideas. The normal and successful operation of this process is clearly evident in the changing drinking behaviour of younger people.

When they first drink they find the experience exciting and liberating. Young people are prone to partying wildly and drinking excessively and they continue to do it for a while. But drinking has its down-sides; hangovers, missed opportunities, accidents and bad outcomes. Eventually the dissonance makes them choose to drink more moderately. Most people grow out of drinking excessively, and bouts of over-indulging become relatively infrequent.

Alcoholics however lack recognition of the down-side of the argument; their automatic processes value the beneficial aspects of drinking very highly and undervalue the detrimental ones. So when first confronted by the dissonance caused by the evidence supporting "drinking is good" vs "drinking is bad" it is pre-determined that they will favour "drinking is good". But the evidence that drinking is bad doesn't go away, it slowly escalates.

Over time, as their addiction strengthens and drinking increases, the evidence that drinking is bad mounts and the dissonance this causes increases. The distress caused brings the issues to the forefront of our minds so that we can resolve them, but with the alcohol issue there is a major problem. The "drinking is bad" side of the argument has words, events, places and people associated with it; it is evidence based. But the "drinking is good" side of the argument doesn't have words, it has feelings; and you can't negotiate with feelings. You can protest and challenge as much as you like, and construct the most persuasive of arguments, but the feeling persists.

The issues cannot be reconciled. They remain, they grow, and the distress constantly brings them back to mind.

At this point the alcoholic's mind moves to reduce the distress caused by the dissonance, and creates justifications that minimise the contradictory viewpoint. This happens automatically. It is not a deliberate thinking process; it is the brain adapting to try to remove a problem.

Over time though the evidence that drinking is bad mounts and the stress felt due to cognitive dissonance becomes enormous. The distance between the opposing viewpoints becomes huge, the weight of each position grows in magnitude, and the minimising justifications begin to fail to remain plausible. On the one hand there is "alcohol is the only thing that makes life worthwhile" on the other hand is "alcohol is destroying my life". The conflict is enormous, but the "alcohol is good" argument has its origins directly in the subconscious circuits of the brain and communicates through powerful feelings, so it prevails. Lee's mind will continue to attempt to reduce the distress by minimising the idea that drinking is a bad thing; but as their addiction deepens these justifying arguments fail to pacify, and the dissonance rages... unless they drink.

It is easy to discover whether or not Lee has reached this point. You simply have to comment that they are drinking too much and listen to the reply.

Typical defences are:

- – Problem? WHAT problem?
- – I'm not THAT bad!
- – All I want is a little relief!

- I'm not hurting anybody but myself!
- You're not so pure yourself!
- I can stop any time I want to!
- I'm not nearly as bad as OTHER people!
- If you understood my problems you'd drink too
- Nobody is going to tell ME what to do!
- I don't have time (or money) to get help!
- I'll handle it myself!

All alcoholics face this period of extreme inner conflict, when the primal demand that they continue drinking is challenged by the mounting evidence that their continued drinking is disastrous. But there is good news in this. If Lee's response is delivered irritably or angrily, or if your comment is dismissed huffily, then this means you have touched a sore point. For it to be a sore point then Lee needs to be suffering from that cognitive dissonance, and they only suffer that when the two conflicting beliefs are present. This means that Lee is realising that their drinking isn't all good after all... that it is doing harm that can't be successfully brushed aside.

The good news is that they are aware (even if they will not acknowledge it) that their drinking is causing trouble. It is a beginning.

Until they have reached this point then there is no possibility whatsoever that they will stop drinking of their own accord since they simply have no reason to do so. Until then their entire experience and belief is that drinking is good, and that there is little if any down-side. It is a terrible thing to have to say, but until the down-sides of drinking become undeniable to them there's absolutely nothing you can do to help. You can beg and plead, and perhaps they will (appear to) slow down their drinking for a while to appease you, but they will not be able to stop. They will hide their drinking better, and they will lie to you, but stop drinking? no! they cannot. The primal and wordless demand to drink is irresistible until they fully recognise within themselves that they have a serious problem and that a fundamental change is essential. Only then do they have a chance to intervene successfully.

Denial is a complete barrier to overcoming alcoholism. Until Lee accepts that their drinking is a problem then as far as *they* can see there is no problem to be solved. This is the worst time possible for you. Until they start to recognise that alcohol is a problem then they are beyond help, and further decline and destruction is inevitable. But most alcoholics and addicts *do* recover. Unfortunately though they have to take the downward escalator quite a long way before the pain of continuing exceeds the pain of stopping, and only they can choose when to step off. For the most part you can only sit and watch that happen. However, while the choice to change can only be made by Lee, you are not completely without influence, and there are things you can do in this time to help yourself.

Lee's drinking has an effect on you. You need to look after yourself, and maybe others, and take what help you can. You will need to be both strong and prepared for what lies ahead.

You should tell someone about your concern and seek help. Go and visit your doctor to see what they can recommend. You need some relief from the burden you're carrying and you have a pressing need not to keep this burden to yourself; both will cause you a great deal of stress. There may be little the doctor can do directly, but the visit will still help you. The old wisdom that "a problem shared is a problem halved" is correct, and you will feel better for sharing your concerns with someone else. While there's little the doctor can do to intervene without Lee's cooperation they should be able to refer you to other services that are available, and you should research these; you will want to have these at your fingertips when the time comes that Lee is ready to consider change.

The other avenue you should explore, if it is available in your area, is Al-anon. Al-anon is a "worldwide fellowship that offers a program of recovery for the families and friends of alcoholics, whether or not the alcoholic recognizes the existence of a drinking problem or seeks help." It was established by the wife of one of the founders of Alcoholics Anonymous, and it is in the same vein; recovery through spirituality... but don't be deterred by that. It is rather old fashioned, and a bit "church-y" but there are people there who can help you enormously.

The people who go to Al-anon have partners, spouses, family members or friends that have drinking problems, either currently or in the past. You will find you are not alone in your situation; there are very many others. They will give you advice on how to cope yourself, and how to help Lee. You will find people there whose partners have been exactly like Lee, but who have recovered and are now sober, and you will find people like yourself struggling with an alcoholic that's still drinking. They will want to help you if they can, and it is free.

Al-anon can help you in ways that professional counsellors can't. The people in Al-anon don't have the knowledge of book-learning; they have the wisdom of experience. As was said, the organisation can seem a little strange, but take from it what is offered freely and leave the parts that don't suit you; no-one will think the less of you for that.

The first challenge

Stopping drinking is incredibly difficult. The mental processes driving addiction are not chosen, they are automatic. The processes are not optional, they are mandatory and involuntary. These processes are impossible to ignore because they directly manipulate how we feel, and they cannot be turned off.

A half-hearted attempt at stopping drinking will fail. It takes absolutely everything the alcoholic has to overcome the power of these essential survival mechanisms with only intellect and willpower. If Lee is to successfully stop drinking then they will need to set about the challenge without reservation.

Lee has no control over their drinking, and you have no control over that either. But if Lee has become very sensitive about their drinking being criticised then you have something you can work on.

You can't change their mind for them, but the things that you say are heard, and those things can influence when Lee is able to escape the downward slide. At some point the balance in Lee's mind has to tip from favouring to continue drinking, to wanting things to change. At some stage most alcoholics will reach this point and recover, but usually only after they have left a colossal amount of damage in their wake and accumulated a huge burden of guilt and shame. It is better for you, Lee, and everyone else in Lee's circle if they can change direction sooner rather than later.

The balance of Lee's mind has to tip from thinking that drinking is good to thinking that drinking is bad. They have to realise that drinking is doing more harm than good. They have to realise that they can't drink a little; if they drink they drink excessively, and they have to *want* this to change. If you are asking an alcoholic to stop drinking then you are asking them to resist some instinctive survival instructions. They can't do this unless they are completely committed to the effort.

Some recovery circles suggest that you have to reach "rock bottom" before the balance will tip, but this isn't true. What is true is that left alone many alcoholics will lose almost everything before they realise that a fundamental change is necessary if they are to survive. But Lee is not alone. Lee has you and probably others that want to help.

If Lee is to recover then the balance in their mind has to shift from thinking that drinking is good to thinking that drinking is bad, *and* they have to realise that this means stopping drinking completely; forever. This is a huge change in direction for someone who believes that drinking provides the only relief from an otherwise unbearable world. You can help that happen, but it isn't easy.

Remember that Lee's thinking is not measured and rational on this subject. You can't simply discuss the issue with them, deliver relevant information, and expect that they'll reach a different conclusion. Their thoughts are dominated by mental processes that are beyond their control. Their minds are actively defending continued drinking even if they know in their hearts that it is causing problems. Even if they'd like all the trouble that comes from their drinking to go away, there are still two more barriers to be overcome.

The first is that in all their experience, and despite their best efforts and intentions, they cannot moderate their drinking. Nor can they stop for a few days. Their entire experience is that it is impossible to stop drinking. So even if they want to, they don't believe that they can.

The second barrier is their perception that "drinking is fun". Each time they have taken their first relieving drink of the day they have had a rush of dopamine flow through them. It gave them a strong sense of ease and comfort. But this dose of dopamine also triggered the event to be remembered as good and beneficial. Over the course of time this message is imprinted more and more firmly in their mind. This has been repeated so many times that it is very deeply learned indeed, and drink has become extremely highly valued. To Lee drinking is not only good, it is good far, far above anything else. As they withdrew from all activities that didn't involve drinking it has become the only "fun" they can recall. This is not a rational thought, it is entirely automatic and involuntary, and it is not expressed in words it is expressed in feelings. This is one of the reasons Lee finds it so difficult to talk about drinking badly; they can't explain why they do it.

When you suggest that they should stop drinking what Lee hears is that you want them to give up fun for the rest of their life. You are saying that they will re-find better fun later, but this is an unconvincing argument. The reason it is unconvincing is again down to an instinctive survival mechanism. You will recall "delay discounting" that was mentioned earlier. It is the mechanism we all share whereby we prefer to take an immediate and lesser advantage rather than wait for a greater one, and this is particularly strong in addicts. Lee's brain does not recognise the value of better fun in the future; it automatically rejects it to prefer a little fun now.

To be completely without alcohol is unimaginable to Lee. A life without alcohol means a life without fun... forever! And that is a terrifying thought. Who would willingly choose this option? To be willing to give up fun forever requires that the alternative is even worse.

Despite all the difficulties, it *is* possible that they will choose to stop drinking, and the evidence is very simple; most alcoholics *do* recover.

Tipping the balance

You will know when you are able to start to help Lee, and that is when they respond angrily or dismissively in response to comments about their drinking being excessive or unwelcome.

If the response comes back sharp and immediate then there is little or no deliberate reasoning behind it, it is reactive and straight from their subconscious thoughts. This means that they are sensitive to the subject (i.e. the dissonance is already strong) and that they didn't have to think consciously about justifying their actions; the justification was already present.

At this point it is possible to start helping them, but what follows comes with a caution. When challenged with the truth of their condition, and the change they should make, they have two clear choices; confront this demon, or run.

Running away is one of the defences constructed by addiction; if they could just get away from all their problems then they wouldn't drink so much. It is not true. If they move they will still drink as much because they aren't drinking because of their problems, they're drinking because of their addiction. They don't escape if they go somewhere else; they take the addiction with them along with all the problems it brings. Nevertheless, it appears true to the alcoholic, and it seems to be a way out of their problems; many take it, often several times. At some point Lee will face this question... "Should I stay, or should I leave?" The truth is that they are choosing to either continue to drink or to try and fix their problems where they are.

You have no control over how Lee will answer this question, and not all marriages, relationships or friendships survive this period.

What you need to know very clearly indeed is that you are neither responsible nor accountable for Lee's choice. If they choose to leave then it is exactly that; their choice. If they leave then they leave so that they can carry on drinking without the burden of being told it is bad.

Their running away may leave a hole, but it is not entirely bad. Indeed it can be its own small blessing as the damage caused by their drinking will stop. Not only that, but often having left an alcoholic grieves for what they have lost, and it becomes the single thing that allows them to truly see that their drinking is harmful and has to stop; but this is not guaranteed to happen.

You also have the choice to leave. Alcoholics in the depths of their addiction do terrible things and you may no longer be able to cope with that. If you can't, then leave. An alcoholic may feel in some twisted way that they have the right to destroy their own lives if they choose to, but they do not have the right to take others with them. If you need to, then leave. Perhaps you will be able to help them later, or perhaps your leaving will be the impetus they need to make a change. Either way, they have no right to continue to make you suffer. If it becomes unbearable then cut your losses, and hope for a change. It is they who have the problem that needs fixing not you. You don't have to go down with their ship.

If neither you nor Lee leaves then there are things to do to try and bring forward the time that they become able to change. There are three things that have to change in Lee's mind for recovery to begin to be possible.

They have to believe that:

- A future without alcohol is worthwhile
- Stopping drinking is essential
- Stopping drinking is possible

You cannot make up Lee's mind for them; they have to do that for themselves. But you can encourage that to happen sooner rather than later. The weight of argument required to achieve this is enormous as it has to cause a complete turnaround in Lee's thinking. But by repeating and repeating simple and consistent messages you can make them come to believe they are true. This is how propaganda works.

Lee feels impossibly trapped. They think they should probably drink less, but have learned that they can't actually do that. They also can't imagine a life without alcohol... it's just too awful a prospect to consider. So they don't *want* to stop drinking (they don't believe it's possible anyway) but they desperately want the problems that accompany drinking to go away.

You have to talk about their drinking to make them think about it more at a conscious level. You have to make them inspect the evidence more closely as this will slowly erode the misinformation and excuses their mind is generating. Most importantly you must show Lee that there is a possible way out, and that the way out leads to somewhere better. This is a very frustrating and slow road at first, and the things you say will not be welcomed. But while you have things that must be said you also need to be a little careful about when you say them.

There is no point whatsoever in trying to discuss their drinking while they are intoxicated; that's when they will be at their most argumentative and there's a good chance they won't even remember what you say. But still, don't let them get away with thinking it's un-noticed or acceptable (but don't get into an argument either, there's no gain to be made from arguing with a drunk). Say just one thing they should think about, but don't let that one thing be an accusation of them being weak or bad.

Here are some examples:

- I'm worried about you having to drink so much these days
- Drink seems to have got a hold of you
- This is happening more often than it used to

The times they are slightly dulled with a hangover can be a good time to talk about their drinking as they're less mentally agile and can't argue back quite so successfully.

You need to work on both sides of their dissonant ideas; make the "drinking is good" side less convincing, and make the "drinking is bad" side more convincing.

Talk to Lee about how alcohol affects the memory of some people. Explain how they only remember good things about drinking, and not the bad things. Be sure to be clear that it is alcohol that does this, not the person. You need to explain to Lee that they are probably one of these people, and because of this they don't put correct emphasis in the down-sides of drinking; it's how alcohol works in people with certain characteristics. You also need to talk plainly about these down-sides. Invite Lee to look at some of these closely and try to find the truth in them.

As you highlight the problems their drinking is causing then you will dramatically increase the dissonance as you put more and more evidence on the side that says "drinking is bad". Eventually this side has to be so overwhelming that the "drinking is good" side collapses, but while Lee feels trapped in-between then the only option they may see is to run, so you also need to show a way out of the trap.

- What Lee knows is that they do terrible things that are out of character, and can't understand why. Let them know that their mental processes have been hijacked by alcohol, and that much of what they do is beyond their control. They are not bad, they are ill.
- Let them know that losing control of drinking is very common. It is not weak people that get caught in the alcohol trap, it can happen to anyone that has certain mental characteristics
- Let them know that most people *do* become able to stop drinking (even though it's incredibly difficult) once they understand the nature of their condition
- Let them know that most people trapped by drinking recover and go on to enjoy happy lives
- Lee expects that the term "alcoholic" is an insult. Let them know that an alcoholic is someone suffering from alcoholism (addiction), and that this can be successfully treated if they want it. In time they won't recoil from "alcoholic"; they'll come to accept it as describing them. I.e. they have an illness that should be treated
- Let them know that their memory is corrupted, and that fun does still exist without alcohol... it's just that their memory presents a faulty view.

Listen carefully for the occasions that Lee says "I drink because..." Whatever they said next is a justification of their drinking but not actually the reason. You need to counter their statement pointing out that their mental processes have been hijacked by alcohol. They may believe that what they said is true, but it isn't. Their thinking has been corrupted by alcohol. They are compelled to drink alcohol by a force that's beyond their deliberate control. Say that you understand how it works; that they don't drink so much because they *choose* to, they drink because they *have* to. Alcohol has corrupted the mental process that gives them choice. The only correct end to the statement "I drink because" is "I have to".

Say the things they have to hear in small and short increments. Be clear, be consistent, and be persistent, but above all be brief unless they want to talk; if they do, then *let them unload*.

You are making Lee extremely agitated by talking about their drinking, so especially at first keep it to a few lines and no more. What you say will probably be rejected out of hand, but the words will not be forgotten; you are striking at a raw nerve, and once the ideas are planted they are seeds that will grow. It is going to take time for these ideas to take hold as they run contrary to opposing ideas that have been laid down and reinforced over the years. Also, while you are presenting Lee with true facts that may build and combine to make some sense, they do not counter the wordless "gut feel" that screams back "noooo!" to everything you say.

It is a hard and slow road and you are often going to make Lee angry when you raise the subject; but keep going, you are reversing the positions of their dissonant ideas and showing them a way out of the alcohol trap.

Your aim in these short conversations is to establish hope; hope that there's a way out, and hope that a better future is possible.

You also have to continue to raise the contrary side. Lee will be *extremely* sensitive to this, but you must raise it anyway. There are bad consequences of their drinking, and they need to be stated.

Every time you identify a way that their drinking is a problem you add confirmation to what Lee doesn't want to believe... but that confirmation happens anyway whether they want it or not. Say it in different ways, say that you're speaking out because you are concerned for them, say that they can become well again and get control of their lives back, but say it, and keep saying it. Say that their drinking is a problem. Say that their drinking is increasing. Say that they are drunk more often than they used to be. Say that they're doing bad things while drunk more often. Say that they become a different person when they drink and that person's not nice. Say that it seems like they've lost control of their drinking. Whatever issues their drinking is causing then mention them. But always, always, always blame the alcohol, not Lee.

You are going to cause great distress in Lee as they wrestle with what you are saying. If you see this distress then it is working, and a day will eventually come that their mind teeters in the balance.

If they start to speak about their drinking then let them talk. Don't feel as though you have to say anything back as your silence will encourage them to say more. Keep your attention completely focussed on them, and look them in the eyes. If they are talking about their drinking then they are breaking open secrets. They get a personal lift from this, but they are also giving you ways to talk about their drinking again; if you've been told things then you implicitly have permission to mention them again.

In your responses it is essential that you show compassion, not blame. An alcoholic is ill, not bad, and you need to shift Lee's experience on this. You also want to encourage them to be able to talk about it again, not discourage them, so use expressions like "I know", "that sounds terrible", "I'd heard about that", "does it always happen like that?" to keep the conversation going. The more they can tell you, the fewer secrets they hold. It will make them feel lighter, and it will make the subject far easier to re-visit.

At the end of the conversation thank them for confiding in you. Assure them you are there for them and will help if they want you to.

It can take weeks, months or years to reach this point, so you need to be as patient and persistent as you can manage. Lee is going to resist you all the way because they are driven on by those misconnected survival mechanisms. But there will come a time when Lee begins to open up, and the subject becomes discussable.

You need to listen for two things in particular. You need to recognise when Lee is exploring the possibility of getting out of the alcohol trap they are in, that a better future might be possible, and you need to look for signs that they are becoming willing to accept help.

On the point of a better future you have these key points to make.

- When (say when, not if) they stop drinking much of their stress will drop off and they will become happier. You have a whole conversation you can have on how alcohol changes the brain in terms of dopamine and stimulants
- Everyone likes them more when they're not drinking
- Their constant fear, guilt and shame will disappear

- It is difficult, but most people with drinking problems *do* overcome them and return to having happy and fulfilled lives
- You will help them

On the point of willingness to accept help you are looking for some quite subtle things. Are they becoming inquisitive about how you know so much? Do they ask where to find out about these things? Do they ask you to prove what you're saying? Anything like this indicates that denial is faltering. They no longer completely reject what you are saying; they are now testing to see if it's true.

You now need to elicit one comment from them upon which denial is broken. You need them to acknowledge that they have a drinking problem.

This is a hard one to tease out, but you can try this when you think they're close.

"Your drinking problem's quite bad isn't it?"

If they don't immediately reject the suggestion then denial is collapsing. Resist the silence and wait.

If they can bring themselves to say "yes", even though every fibre of them is screaming "noooo!" then they are ready to be helped.

It is a huge milestone, both for you and for Lee, and once it is said then it can't be taken back. For Lee it means they can talk about something they've kept as a secret for a long time, and holding that secret has hurt great deal. It means you can talk freely about what can be done to help fix their drinking problem. You can help Lee understand their condition; how it developed and how their mind is lying to them. You can now talk about doing the things that will make Lee better, and you can start planning them together.

It is the moment when things turn from getting worse to getting better, and it is a life changing moment. A few tears won't hurt.

Preparing to stop

Breaking their addiction is one of the hardest things an alcoholic will ever attempt. The challenge lies in the very nature of the addiction. The forces that compel them to drink are at the instinct level. These are the forces that make us run from wild animals, withdraw from danger or seek out a safe hiding place. They are primitive and very powerful; they demand that we take action to secure our survival. The demand is presented as feelings and emotions, not words, and these feelings are presented without reference to the rational, thinking parts of our brain. They come without our permission, and they cannot be negotiated with; you can't stop an emotion by debating with it.

The fight with alcoholism is a battle within Lee's own mind. There are feelings and emotions that insist that they drink. They try and overcome these with logic and willpower. But it is not a fair struggle, and it is extremely unlikely that an alcoholic can recover alone; the insistence that they drink is relentless and pays no heed to the evidence that they must not. Even while their conscious minds say "I mustn't drink, it is killing me" their feelings are screaming "drink! drink! drink!".

It is not an evenly matched fight. Willpower and determination are not infinite and the odds favour instinct over a compromised free-will. The alcoholic's battle is fought with their own mind. The illness is therefore precisely as clever, cunning, deceptive and determined as they are; except the illness is also armed with feelings that incredibly persuasive. This is why stopping drinking is so difficult, and why it is nearly impossible to achieve alone. For an alcoholic to break their addiction they must really want to, and they need the boost of outside support.

There are very many ways to get sober, but no single method is statistically more likely to succeed than another. In fact the success rate of any treatment type is disturbingly poor. The likelihood of an alcoholic staying alcohol-free for a year after attending a treatment centre is about 5%. The same is also the case for AA or trying to get sober at home.

The critical factor is not the recovery method itself, but the willingness of the participant, and this is your biggest challenge.

If Lee is to successfully break their addiction then they need to throw absolutely everything into the effort; anything less will be insufficient. There has to be absolutely nothing holding them back. Denial needs to be broken completely and they must have the desire to make a dramatic change... and that change is to stop drinking completely.

Lee has admitted that they've lost control of their drinking and that it is a problem. This has put a crack in the armour of denial. The next step is to continue to dismantle that denial and get Lee to fully believe themselves that they must stop drinking altogether if they are to have a worthwhile future.

You can help Lee build up to this point, but when the time comes that they try to stop drinking then the idea must be wholly theirs. If you harass them into stopping drinking or entering some therapy then this is most unlikely to be successful. If they are forced into stopping drinking by someone else then the intention is flawed; they are not doing it for themselves, but to appease others. They will fail in their attempt. Breaking free of addiction is only possible when the sufferer fully believes that they must stop if they are going to survive or have a worthwhile life. They have to believe that stopping drinking completely is the only option available. This is a huge change for someone whose mind tells them that drinking is the only thing in their life that makes carrying on worthwhile.

Acknowledging that their drinking is a problem is a complete game changer. The issue is now open for discussion, but Lee will still hate talking about their drinking at first... it will hurt terribly. Every time it is spoken about they will feel like a complete failure as a person. They will also feel the weight of their burden of shame and guilt for the things they've done (and not done) because of drinking.

Dealing with the pain of the past will be addressed in due course, but Lee needs to stop drinking first (they must stop making things worse before they embark on fixing up their past). For the moment constant repetition that things will get better if they will stop drinking is sufficient, but once they have stopped drinking then there's a lot of work to be done to stop their past from haunting them and constantly pulling them back towards addiction. This is addressed later but the immediate issue is to get them to decide to try to stop drinking.

You should continue working on these three points:

– A future without alcohol is worthwhile
– Stopping drinking is essential
– Stopping drinking is possible

Keep revisiting the subject, but keep it short until Lee wants to talk. You are breaking down denial and building the foundation their recovery will stand on. This will take time. Keep going.

An illness, not a weakness

Lee needs to become comfortable with the term "alcoholic" instead of recoiling from it. Alcoholic is a label given to someone suffering from alcoholism. It does not impart shame except from those that don't know this. Lee needs to forgive their ignorance; they thought the same too until recently.

An alcoholic is someone who is ill, not someone who is bad. You need to impress this on Lee very clearly indeed. The mechanisms of addiction are described in the earlier parts of this book, and Lee needs to learn and embrace these thoroughly. You need to lay down a sequence of linked ideas in their mind.

- I am an alcoholic
- Alcoholics are people who suffer from alcoholism
- There are lots of alcoholics
- Alcoholism is a mental illness that insists that we drink, and that drinking is good
- The symptoms of alcoholism are:
- Loss of control over how much is drunk and when
- Continued regular use of alcohol despite bad things happening
- Distorted memory regarding alcohol
- It is progressive, and if left unchecked; fatal
- The emotional experience of alcoholism is; fear, confusion, frustration, hopelessness and loneliness
- Alcoholism cannot be cured, but it can be treated
- Fear, confusion, frustration, hopelessness and loneliness can be removed and replaced by peace.
- Most alcoholics recover at some point
- Life can become good again

The value of this sequence of ideas is that it links their problem to a solution. Lee needs to believe that there *is* a pathway out, and that the gain *is* worth the cost.

There is an important caution that needs attaching to recognising that Lee's problem is an illness, and that is that being an alcoholic does not excuse their actions. It may explain them, but it does not excuse them. If someone at work does something that results in someone else getting hurt, then they are still responsible for that injury even though they didn't intend to cause harm; they should have been more careful. The same principle applies to alcoholics. They are responsible for both their own actions and their recovery. The onus is on Lee to take the necessary steps to make their actions acceptable to society and themselves. Being an alcoholic does not excuse their behaviour, it imparts an obligation to change it.

Engaging help

Lee knows that stopping drinking is difficult, but they do not yet know just how incredibly difficult it is. They know it is difficult because there are many, many occasions they've had to curtail their drinking; and that hurt. They know that they've tried to stop drinking; for an afternoon, for an evening or for a few days, and failed to sustain that determination. They also know that they can't limit their drinking to "just a couple". They have tried and tried to do this, but can't control their drinking. When it comes to drinking it is all or nothing. Continue to impress this on Lee. Either they carry on drinking, and everything in their life gets worse and worse until they die, or they stop drinking completely.

Lee knows that stopping drinking will be difficult but has not yet experienced the full power their mind will exert to try and force them to drink. You can get help if you want to stop drinking, and you should encourage Lee to take all help available (you already have a list of some of the options available to them from your visit to the doctor). The cravings at their peak will be incredible, and cannot be negotiated with, they can only be confronted. Anything that can help Lee through this period will be worthwhile, and there is medication available to help.

Encourage Lee to seek medical advice. There are two reasons to do this. The first reason is the obvious one; that they may get some help, but the other is important too. If Lee shares that their drinking is a problem with someone else, then it further secures in their mind that they have a problem that needs to be overcome. It makes them more accepting of their position and moves further away from denial. But Lee is not going to commit to this easily. Even though their minds may be saying "yes, I have to do this", their feelings are still screaming "noooo!" You may need a little subterfuge.

If you see an opening in your discussions with Lee then act immediately. Say that you'll make the appointment for them to discuss their drink problem with the doctor. You can offer to go along too if they'd like. If Lee will let you, then call the doctor to make the appointment yourself. Make the doctor aware that Lee is there to discuss their drinking problem and what they can do about it.

The more broadly Lee confides that they have a drinking problem (and that they are going to do something about it) then the more they accept their condition, and the more their course becomes committed. But the idea of talking to a relative stranger about their drinking problem will be extremely uncomfortable for them. It carries with it that terrible feeling of admitting that you're a failure and accepting the shame that goes with it.

You can change how Lee sees this.

Tell Lee that doctors know that addiction is an illness, so there will be no judgement, and there will be no shaming. The opposite is more likely, that the doctor will be impressed that they've stood up and asked for help. Tell Lee they are not going to the doctor seeking a diagnosis of whether or not they are alcoholic; they already know the answer to that (and only Lee can know this with any certainty). The purpose of the visit is:

- To see if a prescription for craving reducing medication is appropriate
- To find out what services are available to help them

The doctor might go one step further. If someone has been drinking heavily for an extended period then there may be a significant medical risk if they stop suddenly. The doctor may or may not recommend a supervised "detox", where medical help is available through the first days of stopping drinking. Whether or not this is recommended is entirely dependent on the risks apparent to the doctor.

The doctor may also go one step less, and Lee should be prepared for this. The doctor may suggest a course of "controlled drinking" whereby Lee agrees to limit the amount they drink for a while. If you don't prepare Lee for this then the idea will be enormously appealing; a medical professional says they can carry on drinking! But a "controlled drinking" exercise is a complete waste of time and effort. If Lee had the power to control their own drinking then they would already have done so a long time ago; they can't! Lee needs to be ready to answer that they've already tried that and can't... and that they need to stop completely.

There are several types of medication that are available to help someone stop drinking. One makes you violently ill if you take the medicine and then drink. Another reduces the intensity of the cravings. The first doesn't really help much at all. It doesn't reduce the ferocity of the cravings; it just punishes you for drinking, and if you decide you want to drink again then all you have to do is stop taking the medicine. The medicine that claims to reduce cravings may or may not be very effective (it varies from person to person), but the act of taking it certainly is. If Lee is taking some medicine to help, then they believe they are getting help, and that in itself will lift Lee up. A third type of medication interrupts how dopamine works in the brain. This is quite drastic and not without its problems. The doctor will only recommend this through a Psychiatrist and it can only be taken under close supervision.

The doctor may recommend detox', they may recommend a stay in a treatment centre or they may recommend a counselling course. It is up to Lee to choose whether or not to engage these. A great power of this doctor's visit is not necessarily that Lee will immediately choose to stop drinking, but that an independent expert has recommended it. The doctor's opinion is not easily ignored or dismissed, and this contributes strongly to the breakdown of denial.

If you are able to get Lee to ask for help from a doctor then they are well on their way to wanting to stop their drinking. If they have returned with a prescription for craving reducing medication or an appointment for a detox clinic or other institution then they have implicitly said they want to stop. Joy is in order; eat some cake.

AA is free: Give it a try

Whether or not you've been able to get Lee to visit a doctor you should also try and get them to go along to AA.

Alcoholics Anonymous is no more than a group of local alcoholics who meet to stay sober and to help others to do so. AA is not a church, and it is neither a government nor a private institution. There are no doctors, priests, therapists, or counsellors, and there are no leaders. The only people at AA meetings are people that have stopped drinking, and others that are trying to.

If Lee's denial is weakening then you should try to encourage them to go to an AA meeting. They've nothing at all to lose by it, but Lee will resist doing this. Walking into a roomful of strangers not knowing what will happen in there is very confronting. But thinking that you might be seen walking into a meeting and then branded an alcoholic is even worse. You can minimise both of those fears.

AA meetings are full of completely ordinary looking people. They aren't filled with deadbeats queuing up for a bowl of soup. The people in the meetings have, or have had, exactly the same problem as Lee; they are equals. When Lee steps into a meeting he is going to meet kindred spirits, and they are going be welcomed, not shamed. Lee is going to be very apprehensive outside the meeting and fearing being seen going in, but this is founded on the ignorance and prejudice of others and mostly only exists in Lee's mind. It is quite unlikely that anyone seeing Lee will know or care about an AA meeting and *if* they do, and *if* they look down on Lee for going there, then they are simply displaying ignorance. Try to get Lee to realise that if someone looks down on them for going to AA then it is from ignorance; they don't understand that alcoholism is an affliction rather than a weakness. It's not such a big thing to not know though, most don't, so Lee should simply forgive them for that.

The benefits of going to Alcoholics Anonymous are numerous. At AA Lee will see:

- People who used to drink the same way as themselves, but have managed to stop
- That the people that have stopped drinking are ordinary people; they are not especially gifted with some rare strength or talent
- That "alcoholics" appear completely normal; they are not tramps and deadbeats but look like a random selection of people from the local shopping mall
- That recovered alcoholics are relaxed and happy

AA meetings are free (although a collection plate is usually passed around to cover the meeting costs) and they are widespread. The members of AA help each other to get, and to stay sober.

If you can encourage Lee to attend just one meeting "just one... just for me, please?" then you can help them enormously. They will realise they are not unique in their suffering, that it is quite common. They will meet and hear from people who had exactly the same problem. They will see that it is possible to recover. They will see that giving up is worthwhile, and they will be offered help by people that have succeeded in stopping drinking. But Lee will only see these things if they are able to walk in with an open mind; and that is your task.

Lee needs to go there and listen to some people that have managed to stop drinking and stay stopped. The people there are experts in this because they've done it. They have done something that Lee can't. So Lee is there to learn, not to find fault in the people or the method they've used. They should listen for the ideas that will help, and ignore the bits that don't. Ideally Lee will ask for help; advice on how to stop drinking. "How did you do it?" is the only thing they have to say; the rest will follow naturally. If Lee can bring themselves to ask for help then it will be forthcoming.

There are a couple of things you should make Lee aware of though:

AA was founded in the 1930's and is rather old fashioned in its ways and quite church-like. Many people there will talk about how God has made them well. This is the most challenging aspect of participating in AA. Central to AA's program is that the sufferer is powerless over alcohol (which is essentially true) but that God can restore them. Many cannot accept that proposal, but still recover because the concept of God proposed is quite open. AA does not dictate what form this "power greater than ourselves" should take. It is up to the individual to decide that for themselves, and very many in AA do not perceive this "higher power" as being God in the regular Christian sense at all. Very many at AA regard "God" as meaning no more "Group of drunks". Unless Lee already has a strong religious faith you should try to send them there with this in mind.

The other danger is that Lee might use the occasion to convince themselves that they are not an alcoholic. In the meeting people will talk about the things they did while drunk. Lee might seize on a particular example and declare "I didn't do that. I'm not that bad, therefore I can't be an alcoholic. You need to ward this off in advance.

While the illness is common to all alcoholics, the personal experience of it is different, and it is more advanced in some than others. Remind Lee of this. They already know that they can't control their drinking. They don't need to have done the same things while drunk as the others for these things to be true. They are not going to AA for a diagnosis; they already have that. They are going to AA to see if they can get help there.

There is no downside to Lee going to AA. If they get some benefit from it then that is good, they are drawing a whole community behind their effort to get well. If they don't then no harm was done by having a look.

Treatment centres

There are very many institutions offering help for alcoholics who want to recover. Some are very costly and others are free. Some are residential and some take day patients. They vary in the length of the course, but almost all treatments for alcoholics have 2 things in common: they are in part based on AA's 12-step program, and on completion of treatment they recommend 12-step meeting attendance.

Neither AA nor treatment centres has a good statistical record of getting people sober. It is not that the programmes are ineffective; it is to do with the timing of attendance. If the alcoholic still doubts they have a problem then they see no great need to change. Only when the alcoholic realises they have a very severe problem and that they must change in order to survive can any treatment make progress. If the subject isn't at that point then forcing them to attend treatment, or AA will be of limited benefit. If the sufferer hasn't honestly acknowledged their problem then the time they spend there is committed to breaking down denial and getting them to accept that they are an alcoholic. In the case of a treatment centre this may render the whole treatment course ineffective as the sufferer might perform the exercises set, but still have no deep commitment to becoming alcohol-free in the longer term.

Most people attending treatment centres will drink again within a very short period. Don't let Lee go into this type of therapy until they are already committed to change.

Keep going

As you talk to Lee more about their drinking you need to remain aware that their head is constantly arguing against you and they can't prevent this. While the conscious part of their mind (the part responsible for judgement and decision making) may agree that their drinking is bad and has to stop, their feelings demand that they drink, and that they drink now. Lee can't turn this off.

You are continuously building towards one goal: that Lee will decide to have a try at not drinking. Lee has to reach their own decision to stop, but you should keep pushing them towards reaching that conclusion. Keep talking about the three things that support that conclusion:

- A future without alcohol is worthwhile
- Stopping drinking is essential
- Stopping drinking is possible

The whole time you are building these ideas Lee is confronted with challenge of denial. These take the form of persistent lies in their head... "Perhaps I'm not that bad", "I can probably still have the odd one". These have to be recognised as false and rejected, and that takes time.

The key points to keep making are:

- Your memory is distorted; addiction does that. Alcohol is not good. Alcohol brings bad things not good things
- Your mind is telling you lies. When you stop and challenge them intellectually then the lies are exposed... but know that the lies will still keep coming. Recognise the lies when they come
- You must either drink, or not drink. There is no middle path possible
- Alcoholism is progressive; it will keep getting worse until you change
- Stopping drinking is hard, but lots of people manage to do it
- Life without alcohol is actually good

Eventually Lee is going to decide to give stopping drinking a try. Whichever path they choose to do this be ready to support them. As has been said before, the most important thing is that Lee is ready to change. The nature of the help they choose at that point doesn't matter that much; they have become ready, and all help will progress their cause.

Actually stopping

When Lee decides to try not drinking for a while they are going to need help; they have no idea just how hard this is going to be.

If they decide to choose a residential programme then the pressure is off you for a while. During that time you can mostly only visit and show your support. But if Lee is showing signs of fighting the therapy then encourage them to stay the course. Recovery programmes often require the sufferer to do some things that seem to have no bearing at all on their drinking, but they do. These activities that seem to unnecessarily intrude in their private business are usually working towards reducing the risk of relapse.

If Lee is trying to get sober at home, working with some counselling, and/or recovery meetings, then they are going to need your help. It has been said over and over here just how hard this is and why. But here it is again.

Lee is going to try and overcome instinctive survival drives with willpower, and this is an unlikely proposition. They need to do absolutely everything they can to make their path easier and are unlikely to be able to win through alone. They simply lack the endurance to do so.

Withdrawal

The very first thing to do is to forewarn them of the scale of the challenge. Nobody has ever said that stopping drinking is easy... they've said it was worthwhile, not easy. It is hard. The difficulty is that the distress of the cravings comes from feelings, not words. Earlier the example of a crying baby was given for what a single craving feels like. But when people go through withdrawal these cravings continue for longer and come in waves of mounting intensity. Lee has never felt cravings at their peak; they've always yielded before the maximum was reached. This time they have to face the full force of cravings that roll in one after the other for days and days.

Sometimes the craving feels overwhelming. When someone in withdrawal is on their knees in the bedroom with their face buried in the sheets to muffle the noise as they beg for it to stop... then that's a big one. This is what's coming for Lee, and forewarned is forearmed; tell them it is coming, and tell them that it's far bigger than any craving they've yet encountered. You are not trying to scare them here, you are bolstering them up.

When Lee stops drinking the individual cravings will rise to their peak intensity in a few days, then subside from that peak slowly over time. The timing of this varies from individual, but the onset of the greatest cravings will be at around three days.

By 30 days they will be very noticeably smaller. They decline gradually over time, but never completely go away. Over an extended period they become small and infrequent, and with some confidence of sobriety behind them an addict can dismiss them easily. Very loosely (it depends on the individual) the first seven days is the most challenging, up to day 30 is still very difficult and at day 90 the effort to resist picking up a drink is still significant, but declining steadily.

Cravings come just like waves on a beach; in groups. A single craving rises to a peak, and then subsides; but it is a part of a set. If a single craving is big, then the next one is likely to be big too until the set fades away. Similarly, sometimes the cravings roll in in small sets. But exactly like waves on a beach, every now and again a freak craving comes in out of the blue. These are the really testing ones.

It is hard to give anyone who has not experienced these waves of cravings a sense of what they're like, but this is similar and should work for most people:

> Imagine a very tall fireman's ladder leaning against a building and reaching up several storeys. You have an instinctive fear of heights; most people do. You must now climb as high as you dare up this ladder. When you have gone as far as you can go; when the ladder's swaying, when you are breathing hard, you are shaking

uncontrollably, your eyes are darting around, you're sweating, your head is spinning and your heart is pounding... you must now go three steps further; one.... two... three. Now you must stay there for five minutes before you can go down. Time slows down. It seems to take forever before you can move again. You hang on tight, trembling until you can start to make your shaky way down.

The lower you get the easier you feel but when you get to the bottom your heart is still racing from the adrenalin pumping through you and you are panting, sweating and shaking. You probably feel like a stiff drink would help, but you can't have one. Not this time... not ever again!

After a few minutes you have to go up the ladder again. This time you have to go even higher. It is excruciating and the panic is nearly uncontrollable, but you must keep going up even though your mind is screaming "go down!", "go down!" ... but you must still go higher... you must! You wobble and shake as you step on the rungs that take you even higher than before. The world is a swirl of panic, and you hang on frantically until you are allowed down again.

This is the intensity of waves of cravings. There are no words, only intense feelings experienced as naked, raw and imperative compulsion. It is as urgent and demanding as pulling your hand from fire or struggling to the surface when held underwater.

Lee needs to be prepared to confront this when it comes and be assured that the intensity will fade if they just hang on. It isn't forever, it will stop. But there are also some things you can do to help them through these times.

If Lee can do something fully to occupy their mind as the craving comes then the amount it rises and the time it persists can be shortened dramatically. Take some time in advance with Lee to prepare some distractions. These need to be tasks that require a high degree of concentration: manual tasks that are intricate and detailed, problem solving, designing, inventing, creating; anything that demands their full attention. It may be that the craving is so intense that it is impossible to concentrate enough to perform the task, but even the distraction of attempting to will diminish and shorten the craving.

Changes

Lee's mind and body have adapted to a daily barrage of alcohol, and when they stop drinking this equilibrium is abruptly upset.

One of the ways the body responds to large and regular doses of alcohol is to produce more stimulants. This counters the slowing effect of alcohol on the brain. But when there is suddenly no longer any alcohol present then there is just as suddenly no need for this extra stimulant. However, it takes time for the body to adjust and find a new equilibrium.

When Lee first stops drinking there is a massive oversupply of stimulant flowing through them; far more than the body needs now that alcohol isn't present. You will see this in them as uncontrollable shaking, but there are invisible effects too. The stimulant is present to speed up brain function... but now there is far too much. Lee's mind is racing furiously, spinning and churning and thinking... thinking... thinking non-stop. It prevents them from sleeping and gives them the odd experience of time passing extremely slowly. Do you remember how long the last half hour of the school day lasted when you were very young? Lee is experiencing precisely that.

Lee's body will correct this over-production of stimulant and the shaking will stop in a few days. Somewhere between a week and three weeks after stopping drinking the levels will have reverted to near normal levels and Lee will experience sleep like they can't ever recall before; "slept like a baby" will mean something entirely new to them.

The correction of stimulant levels isn't the only change that happens fairly quickly. On top of all the other problems that alcohol causes, it is also a poison which affects the liver, kidneys and stomach. These start to recover as soon as alcohol levels drop away. In a few days you will see Lee's skin colour brighten as they become generally healthier. They are also likely to be standing taller. They won't notice these changes themselves, so make a point of telling them; they need to hear whatever good news there is at the moment.

Lee is going to have a hard time with the cravings. Added to this is that they are generally feeling in low spirits and their mind is continuing to create "reasons" to drink. Feeling down is a direct result of stopping the regular intake of alcohol abruptly. One of the ways that alcohol works in the brain is to fool it into releasing dopamine; that's where the "feel good" of alcohol comes from. But drinking excessively leads the brain to believe that too much dopamine is being produced, so it counters by reducing that. Now that Lee has stopped drinking there is no artificial lift coming from alcohol triggering the feel-good sensation, and instead there is a lower than normal dopamine level. This makes Lee feel down.

Right at the time that Lee is experiencing the peaks of cravings and suffering from sleep deprivation, they also feel miserable. In the earlier stages of withdrawal the mind and body struggle to adjust to the huge change. Lee's brain had been sitting in a puddle of alcohol and their body assaulted by its toxic effects for a long time. Their body and mind had adapted to continue to perform as well as possible under these circumstances, then suddenly, the alcohol has gone; but all the adaptations remain. Lee's brain and body suddenly have to find a new balance, and until it is found there is massive disruption. In addition to cravings, sleeplessness and a racing mind Lee is also likely to experience; anxiety, depression, fatigue, irritability, mood swings, nightmares, loss of appetite, rapid heart rate and night sweats. They have to cope with all of this at a time when they also feel miserable.

Nobody said stopping drinking was easy.

Managing resolve

Lee has to combat withdrawal cravings with willpower, and just as cravings are cyclical, so is resolve. When the craving is small but resolve is high then there's no problem, but when it's the other way around, when the craving is severe but resolve is low, then the likelihood of them giving in to drink is very high. Lee needs to do things that will lift their resolve and avoid things that will diminish it, and you can help them with this. As well as the peaks and toughs of resolve there's also fatigue. Constantly fighting the demand to drink is tiring, and resolve can simply be worn down until there's nothing left to fight with. But there are things that can be done that will boost and restore resolve.

The cravings and willpower only exist in Lee's mind, and these aren't necessarily visible to anyone else. You need to agree some signals with them; they need to let you know when the cravings are getting tough, and they need to let you know when resolve is low (when they just want to give up).

Lifting resolve

Initially Lee is going to have intense periods of feeling low because of the lowered ambient dopamine level in their brain. It takes time for this to regain its optimum level and until it does Lee is going to experience feeling depressed far more often than they feel uplifted. Despite struggling hard and making daily progress they're still going to feel miserable.

You need to explain to Lee that their feeling down is evidence that their mind has been corrupted by alcohol, but that it is now on the mend; this depression will not last forever, and neither will the cravings or other anxieties.

Lee's mind will be jumping around all over the place during the earlier days and weeks of their recovery, and they may be unable to engage in extended dialogue, but if they are then you have an opportunity to stand them up again.

The best way to help is often just to listen, and it is far more powerful than you might expect.

We evolved to live in groups, and the leader of the group would be listened to reverently and without interruption. When you concentrate on listening to someone in this way you make them feel important and their internal perception of their place in the social order soars. Whether they realise why it's happening or not, it makes them feel wonderful. Most people like to talk about themselves but don't often get the chance before the conversation is taken away to somewhere else. If you find yourself in conversation with Lee when they are down then give them that inner lift that comes from being listened to.

When they talk concentrate only and exclusively on them, like there's nothing else in the world at the moment except what they're saying. Don't interrupt, don't make judgements of what they are saying, don't respond with anecdotes of similar experiences, and don't turn the conversation to yourself. Keep the focus on them and ask short open ended questions about what they've said. Keep concentrating on them as though nothing else exists. If you can keep this going for 10 minutes or so then you are going to notice a complete transformation in them. They are going to feel light hearted and excited, and will have no idea why; but you have done this to them. By listening to Lee in this way you can cause an enormous lift in their self-esteem. Give Lee your silence, and listen deliberately. You will make Lee feel better about themselves, and this will lift their resolve.

Another way to make Lee feel better about themselves is to tell them regularly (several times a day at first) how well they're doing. Lee's struggle is continuous, even though you don't necessarily see it, and the constant effort they are putting into not drinking needs recognition if it is to be sustained. Recognise their daily achievement "well done, that's one more day under your belt", and keep encouraging them. Tell them that it's worth it... "sobriety delivers all the things that alcohol promised"; "drinking stops you being happy". When they pass milestones, however minor they may seem to you, make sure you acknowledge them. "You made it through a week-end". "You've never been so many days without a drink before, you should be proud".

Lee's struggle is continuous at first so keep asking how they are feeling, then encourage, praise and congratulate.

When they're struggling with a craving then remind them to keep the horizon close; "it will subside soon", "you only have to keep going for the rest of the day". Also tell them that they can get through it, "You know you can do this, you've already done it "x" times". Your aim is to buoy them up enough to delay drinking. If you can get them to keep going for another 5 minutes, 10 minutes, or half an hour, then the peak of the craving will pass and they will regain control.

Replenishing resolve

There are some things that will fully top-up Lee's resolve, and you need to encourage Lee to engage in as many of these as you can and as often as you can.

If Lee is seeing a counsellor then you'll notice that they are always brighter afterwards. The same is the case for any regular alcohol self-help groups; 12-step or otherwise. It is really important to encourage Lee to keep going to these. There will be times that they are low and tired and really don't want to go... but this is the very time that the meeting/session is most needed. Spending time talking about recovery and talking to other alcoholics *always* helps so don't let opportunities slip past Lee just because they don't feel like it. Bully them a little into going if that's what's needed; they won't regret going afterwards.

If Lee is going to AA or other recovery meetings then try to get the contact details of people who've offered to help. Ask Lee for them directly; "just in case".

Exercise is perhaps a surprising thing to suggest for someone trying to stop drinking, but there are several clear reasons to encourage Lee to engage in some regular activity. The first is a very simple thing about feeling good about ourselves. Lee's body has taken a battering from alcohol, and exercise makes us healthy. When we think we are doing something that's good for us then we feel well about ourselves. If this exercise can also be social, then there is another benefit. Learning to socialise without alcohol is discussed in later on, but in the context of willpower and cravings one of the big challenges is time spent alone. This is when Lee will go into their own head, and that will almost always have an unwanted outcome. Time spent in the company of others is time not spent alone. The last and simplest reason to take exercise is that it releases endorphin into the system.

Endorphin makes us feels good about ourselves and is also a relaxant (i.e. it relieves stress), and right now Lee needs both of these. The exercise needs to be enough to get their heart pumping fast for at least 20 minutes, but the nature of the activity doesn't matter at all. The endorphins released will give Lee a boost for up to 12 hours.

Things that damage resolve

Hungry, Angry, Lonely, Tired: HALT. It's an acronym often used to warn people in recovery of things that are going to make them more vulnerable to picking up a drink.

"Angry" gives the sufferer an opportunity to retaliate, and that retaliation will be to storm off and get drunk. It's a hard one to defend against at a time when Lee is irritable and very low on tolerance. The best thing is that they know that this is a risk for them, and that their brain is in great turmoil so they are almost certain to get angry at some stage. They will suffer extreme mood swings and this is also completely normal and to be expected. They will over-react to things that people say and do. When this happens Lee will need time and space to calm down, but in this time they are particularly vulnerable. Let them know in advance to expect that this will happen. When it does come they will need to try and calm down and re-gain their composure. Drinking is not going to change whatever angered them, but the event was mostly escalated by their current irritability and low tolerance. Long term drinking has done this to them. It is temporary and will pass.

"Hungry" should be an easy one to remedy, but is not necessarily so. A normal symptom of withdrawal is loss of appetite. This means that Lee will get run down and lack energy, and sugar is the fast remedy for this. Lee is likely to want to snack on sweet things so have some available. Just beware though that sugar can be its own addiction, and can occasionally become a problem later. However, sugar addiction is far less damaging than alcohol and is much easier to deal with. If it comes down to a choice between sugar and alcohol, then go with sugar. It may be difficult to get Lee to eat regularly for a while, so a supply of tasty snacks and treats are a good idea until their normal appetite returns.

"Tired" is going to happen; it's inevitable. It is a consequence of the high stimulant levels in Lee's brain that are preventing sleep and also low energy from eating poorly. These will leave Lee feeling low, and prone to feeling sorry for themselves. Reassure them that this is completely normal, and that it won't last long. As soon as the brain figures out how much stimulant to release now that alcohol's not slowing things down, then sleep will return and energy levels will come back.

Of the four; Hungry, Angry, Lonely and Tired, it is "Lonely" that causes the most problems. Feeling lonely brings with it a loss of inner strength. But loneliness does not just reduce resolve, it is far worse; it brings on cravings. When we are lonely when we retreat into our own minds and this is when all Lee's unresolved issues will flood back. They will cause distress, and that will trigger cravings.

Managing cravings

Lee cannot avoid cravings; it is their brain demanding that they drink. The cravings will continue until the brain learns that no matter how vigorously it insists, alcohol does not follow; but it never completely learns this. What it learns is that demanding alcohol doesn't work as often as it used to, so it diminishes the importance in acquiring it. But when Lee first stops drinking the cravings will come so close to each other that they seem continuous.

There are medicines available that will reduce craving and if you weren't able to get Lee to visit a doctor before then it's worth having another try. A doctor's visit will achieve several things; it lets somebody else know that Lee has recognised they have a problem and are going to try to stop drinking, it will possibly draw in other support channels, Lee will gain medication that will help with the cravings, and Lee will feel as though they've done something to help themselves. All will help, but in particular the medication, and the act of taking it, will help Lee get past the cravings.

Triggers

Cravings don't occur randomly, they are triggered. Certain circumstances, places, and people get remembered in association with gaining alcohol, and the brain recognises when these are present and initiates the urge to drink. These are entirely automatic processes and once established they are never forgotten. But they *can* be modified.

The brain cannot unlearn things; once we know something it remains known. But the brain adapts to changing circumstances, and in the dopamine "reward" system this is achieved by changing the importance of gaining the reward. When a trigger consistently fails to return the reward sought then the importance of acting on it (the craving sensation) is reduced; there is no point in chasing something all day long if you can't catch it, no matter how beneficial it may be. The brain can't unlearn that a thing that has been identified as important, but the value given to that importance can be updated. It is by denying cravings that the brain changes this. By successively denying a craving the brain learns that the likelihood of reward in response to a particular trigger is small, so the urgency given to acquiring it is also made small. This has to happen to *all* of Lee's alcohol triggers, and there will be very many of these. But every time a craving is denied, then the importance of a trigger is being devalued. It is slow progress, but it happens nonetheless.

Cravings must be experienced and overcome in order for them to subside, but resolve wears down if the cravings come continuously. You will really help Lee if you can help slow down the frequency of cravings so that they can maintain the resolve to fight off the strong ones.

Triggers fall into two groups; those that relate to the circumstances Lee finds themselves in; people, places and events, and triggers that are activated entirely within their own mind.

External triggers

The simplest and most basic trigger that will induce a craving is seeing alcohol; this will automatically induce a powerful urge to pick it up and drink it. Alcohol is everywhere, either directly or in imagery (advertising, movies, television etc.), so this trigger is activated on a very, very regular basis. But the craving induced isn't always of the same intensity; it depends on how close the source is.

Delay-discounting is the mechanism that instructs us to take advantage of a benefit available now to a bigger one available in the future, and the same applies to closeness. The closer you are to something identified as beneficial then the more powerfully you are encouraged to seize it. This isn't a simple linear relationship; it is exponential. As you get closer to something beneficial then you are far, far more motivated to take it.

If alcohol is an hour's journey away then it has little pull, if it is in a nearby building then it is calling, if it is in the same room then it is an insistent demand, but if it is within reach of the alcoholic then the demand to pick it up is almost overwhelming.

If it is at all possible then you need to remove all alcohol from where Lee is living; cravings come often enough without making them both nearly continuous *and* at their most powerful. If Lee becomes aware of alcohol, in a fridge, cupboard or similar place, then it will start calling to them, and if it is close, so the calling will be intense.

In time Lee will be able to tolerate being close to alcohol far better, but that takes months rather than days, or weeks. But it is more likely that if they have the choice Lee will never normally have alcohol in the house again. Even after years of being alcohol-free an alcoholic will still feel the pull of a glass of alcohol sitting right in front of them. But alcohol isn't just present in the home. Lee will have routines and/or occasions that are regularly associated with drinking.

There will be certain times of the day and times of the week that Lee has routinely drunk; e.g. on the way home from work, weekends, sports events, social outings etc. Some of these are a part of everyday life, and Lee has to be able to do these things without drinking if they are to have a worthwhile existence in the long term. To do this they need to experience and overcome the cravings associated with each of these times and change their lifestyle to avoid some of them completely. Going to a bar on the way home from work may be something that Lee never normally does again.

Drinking associated with a certain time of day, or day of the week can be dealt with by a substantial change of routine. That time was wasted; now Lee can do something substantial with it. If you and Lee can identify what day(s) and time(s) are habitually associated with drinking then you can plan alternate activities to fill those times. It may be a good opportunity to get routine exercise, or Lee could devote this time to a new project or passion; like making something, learning a new skill, or contributing to the community. Anything that fills this time in some way and that is constructive and worthwhile will remove this trigger's power.

Social occasions where drink will be present are virtually unavoidable; certainly avoiding these completely and forever will deny Lee of very many opportunities to enjoy life; so Lee needs to be able to attend these functions. This will be difficult at first as Lee has two challenges. First, they know there will be drinking, and therefore the event will have to be endured just as much as it will be enjoyed. The second challenge is that they don't know how to socialise without a drink inside them. This second issue is discussed later.

Lee has to learn how to attend occasions where drink is present. Seeing and being close to drink is going to trigger a very powerful craving; but this is known in advance. If Lee knows about it then they can muster their resolve to match such occasions, so be certain that they are well aware of this possibility in advance. The second thing to do is to initially avoid Lee attending such events unaccompanied if possible. Either be with them, or have someone else with them that can ask them this simple question periodically; "Are you OK?" The third thing is to have a way to leave if that is needed.

If the craving becomes too uncomfortable then Lee needs to know that they can leave. In reality, knowing that they are not trapped will often be enough for them to be able tolerate the discomfort of the craving in favour of remaining at the occasion, but they will not want to linger. Instead of being the last person to want to leave a party they will become one of the first.

Whenever Lee has been to an occasion where there is drinking then be interested in how it went for them and congratulate them. Their brain recognises that no alcohol was forthcoming in response to that trigger, and therefore diminishes the urgency (the intensity of craving) associated with it. Remind them that every time they confront and overcome a craving then they are diminishing its power. So every time they go to an event that involves alcohol and leave without picking up a drink, then the craving induced by such an occasions diminishes. Enduring the discomfort of a craving helps to reduce the problem, and in time socialising where alcohol is present will become far more comfortable. Every time a craving is overcome is progress towards being able to associate freely.

Understanding some things about Lee's triggers can be helpful, but it is only a limited benefit. Completely avoiding the triggering circumstances is not a solution. In order for cravings to subside they have to be triggered and then overcome. Knowing their triggers will be useful to Lee insofar as they can know when to expect that cravings will come, and therefore be prepared to face them. But we live in a world awash in alcohol, and alcohol references are everywhere; in advertising, movies, TV etc. You can't wrap Lee up and keep them away from all alcohol signals for the rest of their life; this is both impossible and counter-productive. Lee has to come to terms with living in a world where alcohol and references to alcohol are commonplace. Alcohol is their problem to deal with, not everybody else's. Shielding them completely from triggering events does not help them in the long run; they have to overcome them to diminish their power. Neither does people altering their own lives to accommodate Lee's problem, but it may help ease Lee's passage through withdrawal and early sobriety. While it may help get through the earlier phases they need to be dropped away completely if Lee is to successfully adjust to an alcohol-free life. This means triggering cravings, but they are manageable once Lee's sobriety grows more resilient and the severity of the cravings subsides.

Internal triggers

While all cravings are triggered by something specific, not all triggers are brought on by the outside world; there are some that Lee will activate all by themselves. Some of these are entirely automatic and beyond their control, but others are summoned. You will be unaware of when these are happening, and this is when the signals between Lee and you are most important.

Alcoholics have two powerful triggers that are general in their nature: if they are feeling down, and if they are feeling anxious or distressed. These are the triggers that trapped them into the feedback loop of addiction, and both of these triggers will start firing constantly when Lee first stops drinking.

- Absence of alcohol at a time when dopamine levels are low means that Lee is going to feel unhappy
- All Lee's "worldly troubles" will rage constantly (fuelled by the stimulant in their brain), causing anxiety and distress

If an alcoholic feels unhappy they crave alcohol, and if they are distressed they crave alcohol. These cravings are completely automatic and beyond Lee's direct control. Lee can't simply choose to be happy, and they can't choose to be relaxed. There *are* however things they *can* do to influence these states.

Spend some time identifying things that make Lee feel better, and in particular things that make Lee feel better within themselves. Prepare these so that they are ready to be engaged when Lee is low. Explore with Lee the possibility of doing some voluntary work; this brings a particularly valuable benefit in that it will make them feel good about themselves in an enduring way. Helping others lifts self-esteem, and when Lee feels good within themselves then their resolve will be high.

Time spent on their own is particularly difficult for Lee so take some time to come up with things they can do on their own that will fully occupy their minds; things that require concentration. This may be challenging at first as the overload of stimulant in Lee's brain will make concentrating difficult, but even if they are only able to keep themselves occupied for small periods it will help. Activities that bring with them a simple "win" are particularly valuable. Are there some tasks that Lee's been meaning to get done for quite a while? Some project they've spoken about but never got under way?

Time spent inside their own head is dangerous for an alcoholic as it is likely to result in distress. The difficulty here is how the brain deals with idle time. The brain likes information to be orderly and all issues resolved. While we're busy doing something then our brain is fully occupied processing for that task. But when our brain is not fully occupied it brings back unresolved issues to consider them further in an effort to achieve closure. For an alcoholic this means that when they have idle time then the conflicting "drinking is good" vs "drinking is bad" issue will return and they will find themselves thinking about alcohol and arguing the pro's and con's. But thinking about alcohol has the same effect in the brain as seeing alcohol. The brain believes that alcohol is close and a craving is launched to urge the alcoholic to acquire it, and acquire it now.

Events from the past that have gone badly are also going to spring constantly into Lee's mind as the brain plays and re-plays the scenes in an attempt to find a better resolution. But the past can't be changed, so the bad occurrences remain unimproved, and dwelling on them achieves nothing but cause distress. The automatic response of Lee's brain to distress is that it is relieved by drinking, so a craving is launched. The more Lee thinks about these issues the greater the distress and the bigger the craving. Lee needs to stop dwelling on issues in their past but this isn't easy to achieve as they arrive unbidden. This will be discussed further later but in these early days let Lee understand what's happening and tell them "It's OK to look at the past, but don't stare". Encourage them to notice which scenes from the past keep coming back, and when those events come back then actively intervene to remove the thought line from their mind. This is done by displacing it with another collection of thoughts, and often the easiest way for Lee to do this is to talk to someone else about anything except this particular issue. People like to talk about themselves and this is always an easy way for Lee to switch out the thoughts running through their own mind: talking to someone will ease the distress and end the craving.

Other things that will come into Lee's mind are the difficulties they are currently encountering in life. Lee may find it difficult to associate all the other troubles in their life with their drinking, but they are very likely linked in some way. Many of Lee's problems are directly or indirectly caused by their drinking, and their ability to overcome these issues is compromised by their continued drinking (time and money have been committed to drinking instead of getting out of their difficulties). Talk to them about these problems. Lee will have instant responses to many of these issues if you suggest that alcohol is in part responsible for them; these are the automatic defences Lee's mind has prepared to secure the continued supply of alcohol. Lee needs to see these problems as they truly are. You don't have to find solutions to these problems; you just need to find ways to move *towards* their resolution. Identify some tasks and get Lee working on these things. They don't need to completely solve a problem to feel better about it, they only need to advance towards its resolution; improving their position is enough to yield a benefit. This will be a very sensitive area for Lee, so be careful how you approach it. The consistent message needs to be that it is the alcohol that is causing the trouble, not Lee. If Lee completes parts of a few of these tasks every day then these days will feel more successful and Lee's mood will get progressively lighter. At each problem advanced there will be a lift. "Do the things you *should* do before the things you *want* to do" is a good way for Lee to prioritise what to do next.

Another less likely sounding way to keep Lee's spirits up lies in this question: "Is there something I *should* be doing for someone else before I do what I *want* for myself?" Helping other people will always distract Lee from their own problems and give them a personal boost. We evolved to be social creatures living in groups; the survival of the group helped our own survival. For this reason we are rewarded with dopamine when we do something that helps someone else. Every time that Lee does something for someone else ahead of themselves then they will get an emotional lift.

The two issues to try and manage here are; keeping Lee's spirits up (this avoids the triggers and lifts resolve), and keeping Lee's mind away from dwelling on their troubles (distress brings on an alcohol craving). You can't succeed in this all the time, and indeed you are not trying to prevent these cravings completely; Lee needs to endure and overcome cravings in response to these triggers to make them subside. Your aim here is to stop them happening all the time so that Lee is able to keep their resolve up enough to overcome the cravings as they come, and they *will* come.

Time alone

The times Lee is alone are the times of greatest risk that they will give in to a craving. It is almost inevitable that cravings will come at this time, and they will come when Lee's resolve is reduced as there is no peer pressure shoring up their adherence level; "no-one will know!" will echo through their mind.

The power of peer pressure should not be underestimated. An extra tier is added to their resolve while the alcoholic is in the company of people who are expecting that they will not drink.

While in such company they are fully accountable for how they behave. This disappears when they are alone, and unless they are engrossed in some concentrated activity then cravings will come. You need to make Lee think about this and spend some time working out ways to minimise their risk at these times.

What can they do to minimise their time alone?

- Go directly to/from work
- If not at home or work then only go to places with other people and without alcohol
- Can they make themselves accountable to someone for the time, place, and money spent while they are on their own?
- If going out, make it known where to and for how long
- Do not carry cash (alcohol purchases will therefore show in financial records)

Stay away from places that alcohol is available. Remind Lee that the intensity of their craving will increase exponentially as they get closer to alcohol.

- Do not go into places where they used to drink
- Do not go into the car park of places where alcohol is sold
- Do not go alone to events/occasions where there will be alcohol

Lee needs to think about the higher risk of time spent alone and build themselves a set of guidelines for keeping themselves safer. They are not preventing cravings by doing this, they are reducing the chance that they will act on them. Cravings are reduced over time by successively denying them, but the craving does not need to have escalated to being intense for this to work.

For example, if Lee is driving along and comes to somewhere they used to buy alcohol, then a craving will be triggered. If they drive past then the craving will be beaten. But if they pull into the car park the craving will increase in intensity and be so much harder to overcome. The benefit comes from beating the craving, not the intensity of it. Driving past is a win, but pulling into the car park greatly increases risk.

As Lee's brain discovers that more and more triggers are failing to deliver alcohol then the prompting to drink will become more devious. Remember that their alcoholism exists inside their own brain, so it is every bit as capable, creative and cunning as they are. There are three ideas in particular that Lee is going to be confronted by. Let them know they are coming, and talk them through the fallacies.

No-one will know

This is not true, and it is also entirely misleading. "No-one will know" suggests that drinking is OK if it is not discovered by others; but that is not the problem to be addressed. The problem is alcohol, not being seen to drink it. Alcoholics learn that drinking excessively invokes shame if people see it, so they learn to drink secretly to be able to drink what is needed and avoid that pain. "No-one will know" is actually about shame, not alcohol. The issue is that alcohol is destroying their life; shame is a by-product of drinking. If they don't drink, then along with so many other problems slipping away, they don't get the shame. But if they *do* drink then the alcohol problem is worsened. If they drink and don't get caught, then yes, they can avoid the shame, but that shame will simply become a different burden; guilt. "No-one will know" does not make drinking ok, it is going to increase their burden of guilt and the addiction will deepen. It is not avoiding the problem, it is making it worse.

Just one won't hurt

Just one *will* hurt. Lee is trying to stop drinking; they are not trying to *mostly* stop drinking. Lee knows that they can't control their drinking; that once they start drinking then they carry on. Their brain knows this too, and tries to use this to secure alcohol.

As you move around with Lee there will be occasions when you see them look at people drinking, outside a sunny bar for example, and become wistful. You can see that they are thinking how nice that looks, and how it would be so good to join them. This is their mind laying the "just one won't hurt" trap. When you see this happening invite Lee to do this:

Lee should re-imagine that scene that looked so attractive, and re-arrange it. Instead of beer and wine on the tables Lee should replace them with jugs of cordial and fruit juice. Lee will find that when they remove all alcohol from the image that they are no longer drawn to it. Lee wasn't being drawn to the happy times they thought they saw and that they were missing out on. They were drawn to the alcohol.

For these moments Lee needs to be guided by the mantra; "One is too many, ten is not enough". This is their new reality. Their problem is not the fifth, sixth or seventh drink, it is the first one. If they have one drink, then all objections to having another will disappear. They know this is true but are constantly urged to find out if that has changed. But yes, it *is* still true, and it will be for the rest of Lee's life; what is learned cannot be unlearned.

This was written in 1939: "there is no such thing as making a normal drinker out of an alcoholic. Science may one day accomplish this, but it hasn't done so yet." It is still true. There is no such thing as making a normal drinker out of an alcoholic. Alcoholism is a chronic illness. Alcoholism can be put into remission, but it is only dormant; it is still there.

But there is another important reason that having "just one" drink will hurt. Every time that Lee has resisted a craving then the importance of that trigger has been reduced because activating the trigger failed to result in alcohol being consumed. But when they *do* drink in response to a craving then the opposite happens. The trigger responsible for the craving gets re-assessed as being successful again. "Just one" reverses the reduction in the intensity of the cravings achieved by resisting them and restores them towards their full power. Giving in to a craving dramatically increases the chances of giving in to the next one too as it is going to be more powerful than the one that made them drink.

This is why alcoholics that begin to drink moderately after a period of abstinence very quickly lapse right back to the very worst of their drinking. This is not something that *sometimes* happens this *always* happens; it is inevitable. You need to pound this into Lee's mind; "don't pick up the first drink!"

Forever!

Of the three self-sabotaging issues guaranteed to rise in Lee's mind this one is the most lingering and most damaging; if left to run its own course it gradually corrodes away all resolve.

The single most dominant piece of information about alcohol in Lee's mind is that "drinking is fun". Every time they've taken a drink they've receive a dopamine rush that has triggered remembering alcohol as a good thing. The idea that drinking is good has been reinforced time after time, and at each iteration the value of its importance has been raised and with that the intensity of the dopamine reward to be given on its acquisition has also been increased.

This has become so dominant that Lee believes that alcohol is the *only* source of fun available to them. To be without alcohol forever is unimaginable; they are condemned to be miserable for the rest of their life until they die. This idea nags and builds up the recurring thought that the sacrifice they're making isn't worthwhile.

This combines with another doubt. Their experience of stopping drinking to date is that it's impossible; they can do it for a short while, but not in the long term. "Forever" seems to be an utterly unobtainable goal. It is absolutely inconceivable that they will *never* drink again; never, ever, not even once, forever.

This idea leads them to believe that failure is inevitable, in which case why delay? If they *are* going to drink at some point again in the future, then why are they torturing themselves now? They may as well go and have a drink now and put an end to the suffering.

These two ideas will grow in Lee's mind:

- The rest of their life is going to be miserable

– Stopping forever is actually impossible, so why bother?

The most powerful antidote to these two ideas is to be found in someone that has been in Lee's position and recovered. You can explain to Lee that their mind has falsely established that the only fun in life comes from drinking, but a recovered alcoholic can say that, despite what they thought, life became good again after stopping. You can say that most people *do* recover from alcoholism and manage to stop, but an alcoholic can say that despite thinking that stopping drinking was impossible for them, they were able to do it. You can talk about what *should* happen, but a recovered alcoholic can say what *did* happen.

If you can find any way at all to get Lee to talk to alcoholics that have recovered then you give them the best evidence possible that what you are saying is true. But even though you lack direct experience this doesn't mean you can't help. Lee's need is both immediate and persistent. Their mind is constantly going to challenge any obstacle to continued drinking, and you need to be constantly re-building their defences.

- "Drinking is fun" is a false memory. Drinking is not fun, it brings bad things
- "Not drinking means being miserable" is not true
- Once you stop drinking you will find enjoyment in other things again

106

Challenging the idea that "forever is impossible" requires persistence on your part. "Forever" is a self-defeating position for Lee. They are looking too far ahead, and the scale of the challenge is so daunting that it appears completely impossible. You need to bring that horizon close, and you need to keep it close.

"Now" is the only moment we have any control over, not the past, and not the future. Our futures are not determined by our past, but by what we do right now in the current moment. The future is made up of tiny increments of "now".

Lee must think about the present, not the future. The resolution of their problem does not lie in the future, but in today. Equally, their previous days of not drinking don't count either. Not drinking for 5 consecutive days does not mean that you aren't called to drink on the 6th. Each day stands alone. You have to bring Lee to think about today, and only today when it comes to drinking.

The challenge is to not drink today. This is a catch-cry of all recovery methods: "One day at a time".

One day is possible. Lee has done one day before, so they know it is possible. It is possible to not drink today because they have already stopped for 24 hours before. They can do this. They can't guarantee "forever", but they know that "today" is achievable.

One day is all that is needed to become sober.

When all else fails

You have spent a lot of time with Lee talking through what is going to happen and preparing for it, but the time may come that despite all the preparations Lee is challenged by a huge craving. Watching someone in withdrawal struggling with an all-consuming craving is a pitiful sight, but they are still not entirely on their own with nothing but willpower. You are still there and there are still things that you can do: Delay, Distract, and Deny.

Cravings pass. They rise in intensity to a peak, and then they fade. The conciliatory message that's often offered is "It will pass". This may sound helpful, but it is not. Yes, it is true that the craving will pass, but this is of no consolation whatsoever to the person suffering in the moment. Remember that this person is an alcoholic. Alcoholics have "delay discounting" that heavily favours the present over the future. Telling an alcoholic that things will be better soon has no appeal whatsoever; they want the solution that is available now! Don't tell them they should just sit there and endure the suffering waiting for it to pass. Tell them to do something to make it pass.

It was suggested earlier that you prepare some ways to fully occupy Lee's mind when the big cravings come. Now is the time to employ them.

Anything at all that you can do to keep Lee occupied through the peak of a craving will help; delay, delay, delay. Remind them that it will stop soon, and *do something to distract them!* … talk, go for a walk, make coffee, wash the car, re-fold the laundry in the cupboard... anything that will give Lee another 10-20 minutes to get past the worst of it. If Lee has been given the number of another alcoholic to talk to when things get hard then get them to make that call; now is the time.

If Lee is begging for a drink and everything else has failed, then your last resort is to deny them the opportunity. Hide their keys, hide their wallet and hide any money including your own. You are going to be *extremely* unpopular for a short while, but they'll thank you for it later, they really will; nobody, not even an alcoholic, wakes up in the morning wishing they'd got drunk the night before.

Every time Lee gets through a big craving then take the chance to congratulate them and remind them of what overcoming a craving means: It means they are reducing the insanity of the ones to come. By beating a craving now they are making things better for themselves tomorrow. It is a win. Put a tick in the box, a star on the chart and break out the chocolate.

It gets better

The period of huge cravings does not last forever. With every craving overcome the power of them is diminished. They still come in bigger and smaller sets, but the intensity of the peaks lessens and so does the frequency. The very worst of the cravings are gone by or before about 30 days, but they are still powerful for months to come. The very good news for an alcoholic is that getting well happens much faster than getting sick.

Alcoholism is "chronic", but withdrawal is "acute". This means that while Lee will remain an alcoholic forever (albeit a non-drinking one), the symptoms of withdrawal are severe but have a limited span. Post-acute symptoms; mood swings, anxiety, and depression, will come and go and can last up to 2 years, but the very peak of withdrawal has passed within the first month. Try to get Lee to reflect on that and recognise their progress; they are sleeping well, they look and feel healthier, and the intensity of the cravings is dropping away. These all demonstrate progress and need to be recognised.

Over time the nature of the problem changes and something seemingly miraculous happens. Recovering alcoholics do not prevail because they get better at denying the cravings. They do not have to fight them for the rest of their lives; one day the cravings simply stop being a challenge.

At each denied craving the power of its trigger diminishes. Lee will deny many different triggers and these will lose their sting. As the likelihood of gaining a reward in response to a trigger diminishes, so does the urgency assigned to it; the cravings caused by that trigger gets smaller. They don't stop coming, but over time they reduce in intensity to the point that Lee will be aware of them, but be able to step straight past them. Lee most likely won't notice exactly when this has happened; it's like we aren't aware of quite when a headache stopped hurting. But it is a wonderful thing when it happens nonetheless.

That day will come for Lee. Let them know it is coming and why. But until then their challenge is still a daily one, so keep the horizon close. All Lee has to do is not pick up a drink for the rest of the day. The other days don't count.

The pink cloud

At some stage after stopping drinking Lee is going to show a dramatic change in their demeanour; they are going to become bright and happy. This is partly due to the realisation that stopping drinking is actually possible; they're doing it! and partly to do with the emergence of hope; hope that the future really can be better. But there are also physiological changes happening to Lee.

Lee's brain has been very regularly exposed to high doses of alcohol which caused dopamine to be released. The brain then recognised it was over-producing dopamine and reduced both the amount being released and the number of receptors detecting its presence. This led to Lee feeling miserable when not drinking; there was no longer enough dopamine normally in their system to make them feel happy or even content in the world.

When Lee stops all alcohol consumption then the brain once more recognises an imbalance and increases dopamine secretion and recognition to find a new equilibrium. Dopamine levels are increased again, but they initially overshoot the mark, and then come back until it is too little again, then increase a little, then drop back a little and so on. The first dopamine overshoot in particular is quite significant and this will put Lee into an elated state for an extended period; several weeks. This prolonged dopamine high is commonly described as feeling like floating through life on a "pink cloud", when everything seems good in the world. You will see this in them. There is no way to know when this will begin or how long it will last, it varies enormously from person to person, but it is perfectly apparent to anyone looking for its onset.

It marks a time of change; Lee's brain is adapting to being alcohol-free once more. But dopamine presence is not the only change. Their stomach, kidneys and liver in particular are changing too. Having to process a huge load of toxic alcohol everyday has stopped, and the body starts to clean up and regularise itself. Lee will feel better physically, but the change is small and incremental and they are unlikely to recognise it themselves, so be sure let them know. Lee's brain is still having a fierce debate between alcohol being a good thing and a bad thing but for the moment the world is a happy place and Lee's troubles seem small. The two triggers of distress and unhappiness don't get activated so often in this period.

At the same time as the brain is finding a new optimum level for dopamine it is also finding a new level for the stimulants; and the two keep bouncing off each other for a while. This is one reason Lee will experience mood swings, and it takes an extended period (months and years) for these to settle down properly.

When the pink cloud first sets in you have something of a reprieve. Lee is on a high and in good spirits. Their resolve is strong; no longer dragged down by depression and fatigue. The cravings are still coming but will be overcome fairly easily with continued encouragement, praise, celebrating milestones, and pointing out the good changes that are happening. But through all of this good time Lee needs to continue to do the things that are helping them:

- Keeping alcohol distant
- Exercise
- Counselling (in whatever form that is)
- Eating properly

There is one major risk in this period, and that is that Lee feels so well that they can believe they have alcohol beaten. It is likely that Lee will feel as though they are now strong enough to have "just one".

It's time to have a chat.

Lee needs to understand why they are feeling good at this time. They aren't on this high because they've conquered drinking; they will never fully achieve that. They are on this high because they are healing and their brain is adapting to being free of alcohol. But that this high won't last forever; Lee will settle back to a lesser level soon. Now is a good time to remind them of the basics:

- Alcoholism is forever. The processes that have been so deeply learned are never forgotten, they are still there. *Do not* re-awaken them
- Lee can't have just one drink. They never could in the past and this has not changed
- The intensity of cravings is diminished by overcoming them, but brought back on in force by giving into them
- Their brain is still telling them that "drinking is good!", and this is still a lie
- While they do not drink their lives are improving, but drinking again will bring back the hopelessness, fear, frustration, confusion and crushing loneliness

After the pink cloud

The pink cloud is a period when Lee's brain is being overfed dopamine, but this will swing back the other way, and a slightly down period will follow. This is a time of great risk,

At this stage it will be months rather than days since Lee last drank and their confidence will build that they have beaten their addiction. They will not know that a period of feeling a little down and a lowered resolve is coming unless you warn them. Lee will be feeling so good during their experience of the extended dopamine high that they may not heed your warning, but the knowledge needs planting. The cravings still come but while on the pink cloud Lee will feel invincible and overcome them easily. This will end and the scale of the challenge will rise again.

The switch from feeling good about themselves to feeling low doesn't happen quickly, the emotional high has a slow fade. As soon as you think you start to see this then it's time to step into action again.

Self-pity

Self-pity is completely corrosive to recovery. "Poor me, poor me… pour me another drink!"

After the huge effort of going through withdrawal and then the high of the pink cloud Lee is going to drop into something of a slump. This will be several months after stopping drinking and quite disorienting.

After months of struggle Lee will have felt they were winning their fight against alcohol, but now with their resolve in decline and cravings still coming they will start doubting again. They need to know that this down phase is coming, and just like the over-correction of the amount of dopamine their brain should have, this undershoot won't last forever either.

After the initial withdrawal phase it is this time that is most likely to catch Lee out. The challenges of "forever" will come back. Lee will feel sorry for themselves and it will seem that life really isn't getting any better, and if life isn't any better, then what's the point in carrying on struggling against drinking? With so long since their last drink, and with recall of just how miserable their life was fading from memory, finding out if they can have just one drink seems really appealing.

You need to reassure them that this down period is completely normal, and that down periods will happen, but they go away... remember though that Lee places very little value on things getting better in the future.

You will need to keep impressing the same truths onto Lee.

Alcoholism is forever

- They can't have just one drink because one drink re-ignites the addiction with all its consequences
- Their life is getting better without drink in it

It is time for Lee to move onto the next challenges, and to make that last statement actually feel true for them.

Stopping is not enough

An alcoholic is trapped into a cycle of repeated excessive drinking and their behaviour while drunk creates a huge burden of shame and guilt. When Lee stopped drinking then they stopped being a drunk, but they remain an alcoholic; all the learned pathways of addiction are still present, and so is all the accumulated guilt, shame and remorse.

If stopping drinking was enough to halt alcoholism then its treatment would be simple; you'd simply lock the alcoholic away somewhere where they couldn't get alcohol, and after the dopamine and stimulant levels in their brain had regularised then they'd be safe to release into the community. For decades exactly this was done. Someone who drank alcoholically would be committed to somewhere where they could not drink and released after an extended period of abstinence. Almost always that person would be drunk again within a few days. Abstinence doesn't arrest addiction; more is needed.

Dry alcoholics are suffering from depression.

Lee has stopped drinking and this has had one significant impact on their general outlook; the hopelessness and sense of impending doom has disappeared. Hope now exists where once there was just hopelessness.

Lee isn't going to particularly enjoy hearing this news, but stopping drinking is only the start of recovery. To become well requires not only breaking the cycle of addiction and stopping drinking, but also cleaning up the mess made in the alcoholic mind, and then living in a way that disfavours relapse. The aim is to reach a position where drinking is simply unnecessary.

Lee's brain has some automated processes that have been deeply remembered and are never forgotten. These exist and operate entirely without Lee's permission or awareness and Lee cannot turn them off no matter how much they may wish to.

There is the deeply remembered knowledge that drinking is fun and that distress and unhappiness are relieved by drinking

For the rest of their life Lee's brain will continue to automatically seek out alcohol and draw their attention to it. If you ever misplace some alcohol then ask Lee where it is. If it is near them then they *will* have noticed it. They will also gulp down drinks rather than sip at them

Alcoholism is a chronic illness; it is forever. Lee can never completely escape the addiction. For as long as Lee remains alcohol-free then the addiction is in remission. But they re-activate it the moment they pick up just one drink. Avoiding relapse is a challenge that lasts a lifetime. All the evidence shows that if an alcoholic stops drinking but does not change the way that they live then at some stage they will drink again.

Addicts have a self-image that has been seriously damaged by their addiction. They need to build a new identity, perspective and social circle where the old addict identity is excluded or dramatically diminished. In many respects recovering from addiction is like overcoming the challenge of a sudden disability like the loss of a limb. The old ways of doing things are no longer available and new ways to live have to be found.

While Lee was on the pink cloud they could see no need to change anything. As they come down from the high and enter this down phase they can be brought to realise that stopping drinking is not enough.

There is more work to be done and it is in two distinct parts:

- Lee needs to remove the emotional burden of their past and step away from their old identity
- They must establish new ways to live that will not draw them back into their addiction

The first of these stops the past from continuing to hurt, and the second lifts Lee's contentment with their place in the world. These two tasks are presented sequentially here, but they can be pursued simultaneously.

Resolving the past

An unresolved past never goes away.

An alcoholic's recovery isn't measured in days since their last drink; it is measured in their mental wellness. Alcoholics are more than people that were habitually drunk, they are people who are deeply troubled by their past. Stopping drinking stops them from being drunk, but the past remains.

Often an alcoholic will stop drinking but take no further remedial action and this is an extremely unsatisfactory condition; they have removed the only source of known joy in their lives but continue to live with all the emotional consequences of their previous behaviour.

While Lee drank they were overwhelmed with shame, guilt and remorse; the cumulative emotions from the memories of the things they so deeply wish they had or hadn't done. Removing alcohol from their system has done nothing to change this. It may be quite a while since Lee last had a drink, but they are not mentally well; they carry a huge burden of guilt and shame and this bears down on them every day. Lee has done (or not done) a great many things that they deeply regret. The burden of shame and guilt is enormous and recurring memories of those things binds Lee to the "old me". They need to be free of this burden to be able to live happily and freely.

In order to understand why these old issues persist, why they continue to hurt, and how to close them off we need to know a little more about how our brains work.

We are only aware of what is happening in a very small part of our brain (about 15%). We have no direct awareness of what is going on in the rest of it (about 85%). The parts of our brain that we are aware of can be collectively referred to as our "conscious" mind, and the parts that operate without out knowledge, the "subconscious" mind.

"Subconscious:- Adjective:

Of or concerning the part of the mind of which one is not fully aware but which influences one's actions and feelings"

There are some very important features of our subconscious mind that are important to recovery from alcoholism.

The subconscious mind doesn't have to process ideas into language or form. This makes it about a million times faster than the conscious mind

- The subconscious mind has no concept of past, present, or future: everything is "now"
- The subconscious mind processes huge numbers of thought lines simultaneously, whereas the conscious mind can only handle a very few

- The subconscious mind cannot distinguish between real things detected by our senses, and things that are imagined. To the subconscious mind everything is real
- The subconscious mind does not distinguish between self and others: to the subconscious everything is personal
- Our subconscious mind manages muscle control, memory and automatic functions (among other things) and critically, it is where emotions are generated

The subconscious mind is blindingly fast, and in it everything is real, everything is now and everything is personal. Our conscious mind is where the higher functions of judgement, intent and determination (willpower), creativity, planning, and decision making occur, and it is where our emotions are sensed. We have direct and immediate control over what happens in our conscious mind. We have no similar control over what happens in our subconscious mind. What happens in there is automatic; learned, but automatic nonetheless, and it is where our emotions are created. Our emotions are *created* in our subconscious mind, but *sensed* in our conscious mind.

Emotions come from the faster subconscious mind and are triggered by memories in the part of the brain that stores information with an associated importance and emotion. When these memories are accessed then an emotion is invoked, the strength of the emotion is determined by the importance assigned to the memory. This process is entirely automatic, it happens independently of deliberate thought. Emotions quite literally have a mind of their own, and it is one that we have no insight into. Within a few milliseconds of identifying the presence of something we know we are not only subconsciously aware of it, but we also know whether we like it or not. For example, it is the regular memory that is used to identify a snake, but the emotional memory recognises that a snake in the back yard is dangerous; and this invokes the appropriate emotion. This happens so quickly that we are fearful before we are even consciously aware of the proximity of danger. Emotions precede conscious thought.

Triggers to drink invoke an emotion; compulsion. When fired they create demand to drink before any conscious thought occurs. There is nothing rational to argue against, it just happens; and it happens quite literally before there is time to think.

All the processes of addiction reside in the subconscious mind. Lee is trying to fight them with the conscious mind, which is a million times slower! Lee is also trying to combat feelings with logic. This makes breaking addiction so difficult as feelings are completely independent of intent; they come automatically from a different part of the brain. Feelings are impervious to reason. Regardless of how well constructed the argument is, the feelings still keep coming.

The brain likes information to be orderly and promotes unresolved issues into consciousness for them to be thought on further. But it doesn't present all these thoughts simultaneously because the conscious mind can only handle a few at a time, and it only presents them when the brain isn't fully occupied doing something important. Unresolved issues in the subconscious compete for importance, and only the most pressing ones make it through to consciousness when capacity exists.

But just like imagining or actively thinking about an event brings back the emotion associated with it, the thoughts circulating in our subconscious also generate the associated emotions; they are not so powerfully invoked, but they are there. Some thoughts invoke positive emotions, and some invoke negative emotions. The balance of these across all the thoughts active in our subconscious mind is what we call our "mood".

We know the thoughts in our conscious mind, but are unaware of the thoughts processing in our subconscious mind. But while we don't know directly what these thoughts are our mood indicates whether the balance of the emotions generated is from good or painful thoughts. Lee may have stopped drinking, but all the issues that cause shame, guilt and remorse remain unresolved. Even though these events occurred in the past, and therefore can't be changed, they are still brought to consciousness because our subconscious minds have no concept of time; everything is now. The issues need resolving as though they are happening right now, and Lee still gets the emotion associated with them; stopping drinking hasn't changed this.

Worrying about the things that are depressing them makes it worse for Lee. Holding on to the thought for an extended period grows the intensity of the associated emotion and depressing thoughts are gregarious. When we dwell on an unresolved issue we not only bring it back to mind but we also bring in any similar incidents to see if they can yield solutions to the current problem. Not only are events with similar circumstances recalled, so are events with similar emotions. When we start to worry, then we bring in more worries. But endlessly thinking through them rarely achieves a breakthrough; if one was to be found it would have been discovered long ago. The problems are stuck fast, and the more often they are recalled, the faster the neural pathways linking them become. Over time they become so accessible that it becomes almost impossible not to think about them. Lee's past will not go away, and the undercurrent of distress is constant.

Lee has an oversupply of unsatisfactory outcomes that keep coming forward to be resolved, and each time they are brought to mind they come with their associated emotions;

anxiety, distress, fear, anger, etc. Even when these haven't broken through to consciousness they are still active and invoke the associated emotions. Collectively they hold Lee in a distressed and unhappy state; the precise conditions that will make Lee yearn for alcohol.

While these memories are dominant they lock Lee into a state of restlessness, irritability and discontent. They believe that they are a bad person and that hurts. Lee has a huge pile of issues, and extremely low self-esteem (although it is most unlikely that Lee will show this externally). Recovering alcoholics have a persistent sense of worthlessness that is not remedied by stopping drinking.

It is time to start removing this burden. For Lee this task is going to be neither easy nor pleasant; in fact it will be deeply unpleasant.

All treatments for alcoholism include this work, whether it is through alcohol counselling, treatment centres or 12-step programs. It is not easy to complete this successfully alone and at home, and if at all possible Lee should seek help with this part. It is *possible* to do this at home, but as someone close to Lee it is likely that some of their past actions may relate to you directly, and this means that Lee can't bring themselves to expose them to you. If they can't talk about an issue then they also can't bring it to closure. This is why these issues are best addressed under the guidance of someone independent.

Having said that, it is not impossible to help Lee through this time, and it is important that you at least understand the key parts of the process, why they are important, and how and why they work.

Lee has to re-visit the *all* the things from their past that are causing significant distress. These issues keep coming back because Lee's brain finds them unresolved; i.e. still requiring action in one way or another. Lee has to visit each of these occurrences one by one and take some action(s) to bring resolution to them. This will prevent the issues from being constantly brought back into their mind, and with that it will stop the associated emotion recurring. As each issue is resolved Lee's mood will brighten a little.

However, some of these events from their past are very deeply shameful, and many will relate to, or have a bearing on those who are close to them. Some of the things that Lee needs to put to rest are considered so shameful that they must be hidden from sight completely. Most particularly it is these that need to be closed as it is these that are causing the most damage. Lee needs to bring these issues out of the shadows to be rid of them, but almost certainly they can't do this with someone they are close to. This can be a traumatic process, hence the recommendation that this be done in conjunction with someone who understands this process and is both confidential and independent.

While this process is painful for Lee to undertake it is also incredibly healing. Once the issues of their past are successfully closed off then Lee will never experience the pain of them again. Lee will still know that they happened, but the issues won't keep coming back and churning away in their mind, because they have ceased to be unresolved. Lee's general mood will shift from being distressed to being content, and this removes one of the most ingrained triggers to drink.

This general lifting of Lee's mood reduces the likelihood that events can conspire to lower Lee's spirits to the point that they will drink again, and this is why this work is so important.

Secrets

"A problem shared is a problem halved" is an old wisdom, and old philosophies that have withstood the test of time and are still used today have something behind them. In this case it is that holding secrets imparts an intellectual and emotional burden.

Keeping secrets is intellectually demanding. The brain knows that each secret is an unsatisfactorily resolved issue, so it keeps bringing them back to mind along with the associated emotion. But secrets have another emotion associated with them; fear. Guilty secrets carry with them the knowledge that if they are exposed, then shame will follow. It is that burden of fear that is lifted in the procedure described here.

The process is simple, but painful to perform. To break the power of a secret you simply have to tell it to someone that doesn't judge you for it. This simple act removes the associated fear from the issue. It doesn't remove or resolve the problem, but it makes it much easier to bear.

That is easy to say, but very uncomfortable to do. The extent to which this process is successful is entirely dependent on having the right person hear the secrets and addressing the big issues that cause distress; and herein lies the difficulty. The issues that most need to be addressed are the ones that cause the most distress when brought to mind. But these are the very issues that Lee least wants to admit. If an issue is withheld then so is its burden. What Lee withholds will continue to hurt; they remain as sick as their biggest secret. To be effective this task requires completeness and this in turn requires brutal self-honesty.

The issues that require closure are not just those arising from what Lee has done, but also things that have happened to them, and these are not only issues relating to alcohol. It is *all* issues from the past that need to be addressed here, not just those caused by drinking.

Alcoholism becomes committed into a downward spiral when the sufferer drinks to relieve distress, and someone with a deeply traumatic incident in their past can reach that point much sooner than someone without. For example, heavy drinking by victims of child abuse that also have the characteristics that pre-dispose them to addiction is far more likely to result in alcoholism than in the average population. But while childhood trauma will increase the chances of a susceptible person developing alcoholism it is by no means a requirement. Many alcoholics will have no such event in their background, but if it is present then it needs to be addressed. This is another example of why the help Lee gets during this phase should be independent; there may be a subject they feel unable to disclose to those that are close to them.

The process involved in breaking the burden of secrets is simple: you make a list of the things that hurt (i.e. they make you wince and squirm inside when they are recalled), then you read this list out loud to somebody. But while the process is simple, successfully negotiating it isn't. It takes three things:

The right listener

Of the three requirements this is the easiest to achieve. We hold secrets to shield ourselves from the critical judgement of others. We hold them to avoid being shamed, and we fear that shame. The person with whom Lee will share these secrets has to be someone that Lee can trust to keep them confidential, but also someone that will hear them without passing judgement (because it is fear of that judgement that has forced Lee to keep the secrets in the first place).

If Lee is in a treatment centre, or undergoing counselling or therapy then these secrets will be broken within the secure confines of patient confidentiality. If Lee is attending 12-step or similar meetings then this process will be conducted under the guidance of a "sponsor", and Lee will choose this person themselves. If Lee is catholic then their priest is an obvious choice as "confession" is a core precept of the catholic faith. Regardless of who hears the secrets the requirement is the same; they must keep what they hear confidential, and they must hear what is said without passing judgement whatsoever.

The idea that this list of secrets has to be read out loud seems unnecessarily cruel and humiliating, but it has a very real purpose. Information is far more powerfully secured in the mind if it is spoken, rather than thought or read. It is also more strongly secured when spoken with deep emotion. Reading information out loud and with emotion (there will be plenty of that on this occasion) is the most powerful way to commit it into the brain.

Self-honesty

This doesn't sound as though it should be hard, but for Lee it may be. Lee has lived a double life for a long time, with one side showing to the world but a completely different one internally. There's a very good reason for this. Lee has done things or had things happen to them that the world deems bad, and they escape the shame of these things by holding them internally and hiding them from sight. If Lee can avoid the pain of exposing these issues then they will. The great concern is that since this exercise is related to stopping drinking and remaining abstinent then Lee may only disclose issues they think are related to alcohol. This is not the case. *All* major issues need to be cleared. If they are not then the enduring pain continues uninterrupted and Lee can never achieve peace.

With respect to the things that Lee has done it is the extent to which these trouble their conscience that determines whether or not they need attention. Forgetting an aunt's birthday when they were a young child is unlikely to be important, but driving drunk with children in the car and having a near accident will. The list of issues does not need to catalogue every single wrongdoing in Lee's life, just the ones that when recalled invoke a strong and adverse emotion; shame, fear, guilt, remorse, grief, anxiety, resentment, anger etc. It is the big ones that cause the most damage and it these that most need to be resolved. But there are some that Lee will be extremely unwilling to expose.

Courage

Of the three requirements to be relieved of the burden of secrets, courage is the most challenging and it is where you can help most. Exposing your darkest secrets and then telling them to someone takes huge courage. But if Lee is to achieve a good recovery this is vital; it is the darkest secrets that are the most damaging and the most important ones to expose. Lee *has* to say what these are; if they are not said then the fear associated with them being discovered remains. It is the biggest ones that Lee will want to keep hidden the most, and you can help them in this respect.

You should talk to Lee about secrets and why it is so important to break them. Assure Lee that you are not trying to discover their secrets, you are not interested in them, but encourage them to disclose them. They are going to do this confidentially, and to someone who is not going to cast shame based on what they hear; the process sounds far more awful than it actually is. It will be uncomfortable, but the discomfort is brief; they will feel lighter once they have done it. When you talk to Lee be sure to spell out why this is done. It is done to lift an undercurrent of feeling irritable and discontented, and this will reduce the likelihood of relapse. Lee is going to immediately feel a lift once this is done *if* all the big secrets are spoken. Anything you can do to encourage them to be thorough will help.

The benefit from doing this work is enormous. It removes an otherwise permanent load of stress and anxiety and will bring ease and contentment into Lee's life, but it is difficult for you to be completely convincing about this. You are able to tell Lee what *should* happen, but if you have access to a recovered alcoholic, then they will be able to tell Lee how breaking secrets and dealing with them lifted them into a contented existence. A recovered alcoholic can describe the benefits of doing this work from personal experience. They can talk about what *did* happen, not what *should* happen. If you know of a recovered alcoholic or can find one that is willing to talk to Lee about this then it will help Lee enormously.

The last word on courage and breaking secrets is that Lee does have a simple way of identifying the really big issues if they are willing to risk exploring their own minds a little.

You will recall that the issues that require resolution are queued up in the subconscious mind awaiting their turn to be presented to the conscious mind for further consideration. This is a way for Lee to identify the pressing issues that are unresolved. First, can Lee recall the things that keep coming back to mind; the things they can't stop just popping back in? Get Lee to record these over a period of a few days. The second thing to try is to get Lee to relax completely;

somewhere where they are comfortable and it is quiet and they feel safe. Get them to sit, breathe deeply and slowly, and close their eyes. If Lee can relax and empty their mind of the day's thoughts then this will create processing capacity in their conscious mind for the troubling issues to be worked on. The principal issues will jump straight in. Problems pull in more problems, and by repeating this a few times Lee will be able to step past the first ones and expose a few more out.

Lee's test for whether or not these issues count as ones to be resolved is this: When recalled do they elicit a strong and negative emotion? If they do, then they go on the list.

If you are close to this process of identifying the difficult issues in Lee's past then there is something important you need to ask them. You are not asking to know any secrets, but you need to be certain that the appropriate remedy is being applied. If Lee is satisfied that they have identified all the big issues from their past then you need to ask them to check their list. "Is there anything on this list that you should get specific counselling for?" Give Lee time for this one to sink in and ask it again a few days later.

If there is some traumatic incident from Lee's past that imposes a huge burden on them then they may need to seek professional help to address this specifically. This check is to pick up if there's an additional mental issue that needs attention. For example, if someone has experienced a severe childhood trauma then their likelihood of becoming alcoholic is very dramatically increased. But try not to be too searching in this; don't go looking for something that's not present.

Achieving closure

The whole work of taking the pain out of the past is difficult and very confronting, but it is enormously beneficial; it permanently closes issues that will otherwise cause persistent suffering. Once rid of the burdens of the past then Lee's worldly troubles reduce to become the regular hassles of life. Lee will be far less stressed than before. They will become more relaxed and far better able to deal with life's challenges as they occur. Occasions when their brain triggers alcohol cravings will reduce, and their resolve to overcome cravings when they occur will be high.

Listing the issues from their past and breaking those secrets is the start of this process for Lee. They will feel a great lift from exposing them, but the list has another power; it shows that the extent of their issues is not infinite. In fact, the number of really big issues that Lee needs to put to rest is likely to be quite small. Point this out to them.

Although Lee has removed the fear of exposure from these secrets they are still issues that will continue to haunt them; they are still unresolved and will still be brought forward into consciousness for further consideration. Lee is going to constantly ruminate over every detail of these events, searching and searching for a better outcome, but none will be forthcoming. Lee needs to bring these issues to closure one way or another, this is the only way to stop them recurring. Lee must either change the problem, or accept it as it is; unchangeable.

Lee needs to identify when it's time to persist and when it's time to accept, and they need to stop avoiding difficult issues; they won't go away on their own. They need to look at each issue in turn, focus on what can be done to change it, and if it can't be changed then it's time to accept that reality; if it can't be changed then thinking on it further is not only fruitless, it is damaging.

As Lee deals with each issue in turn then it will seem like the weight of the world is lifting and they will feel an increasing freedom and happiness they've not known in years. But that freedom requires work, some of which is very unpalatable. Lee will need your encouragement to press through some of this. Follow their progress and encourage them to continue to be honest and courageous; it is these qualities that will allow them to complete what is needed.

The aim for Lee is to bring each issue to a point of closure, to a position where it does not sit in the brain unresolved and therefore keep coming back. At some stage all of the issues on the list need to be brought to a point of acceptance. But before Lee tries to accept something they need to verify that it can't actually be changed. Is there something that can be done that will change this and put it right? If there is, then Lee needs to attend to that, because while an issue can still be changed, then it will be impossible to accept.

Some of Lee's issues can be accepted as they stand, but others need some extra work first. Lee should divide their list of issues into three; things I've done that only hurt me, things done to me, and things I have done that hurt someone else. Each has a different pathway to closure.

Things I've done that only hurt me

These are the simplest to deal with. Events that hurt no-one else and that nobody else is bothered about should quite simply be accepted. The world has moved on and wasn't adversely effected, and no-one but Lee suffers any lasting consequence. Lee should simply look at them closely, one by one, acknowledge the lesson learned, and move on. There is nothing to be done. It's in the past. It's gone. There's nothing to see here, move along.

There are however some things that are so bad that they simply refuse to be accepted, and these fall into two categories; things that have been done to me, and things I've done to others

Things done to me

Some things done to us by other people can cause anger and resentment that simply won't yield to the regular tools of acceptance; our minds demand justice, explanations, even revenge. But at the end of the day the issue is still the same; unless this matter can be brought to resolution then it lives with us forever, constantly being recalled for consideration and therefore constantly hurting. The remedy for this sounds like it is coming straight from the pulpit (and indeed it often does) but it works, and the solution lies in forgiveness. If Lee can forgive the person for what they did, then it is concluded. It is then possible to accept it and put it away permanently. But forgiveness can be a difficult thing to achieve. It is quite possible to do, and it relieves us from the burden of anger and resentment, but it is not easy.

There are three pathways that will help, two sound sensible; the third, bizarre.

The first thing to look at is complicity. Big issues for alcoholics do not often come entirely at the hand of someone else. Very often the alcoholics themselves have been instrumental in causing or inflaming the problems. Lee should look at the issue to see to what extent they brought this on themselves. Did they have a part in it? If so the other party can't shoulder all the blame; they are only responsible for their part, not Lee's. If Lee can identify that they had a part in creating or escalating an issue then this dramatically diminishes the part that has to be accepted.

The second route is to allow people to be imperfect. People are *not* perfect. People make mistakes, people get things wrong, sometimes people do bad things, and some people are bad people. But neither revenge nor justice makes right something that was wrong. Lee is accountable for their own actions, but shouldn't make themselves suffer for someone else's failings. Yes, they are the one bearing the consequences, but it is not Lee who did the bad thing... that's the other person's problem.

People aren't perfect, and life isn't fair. Instead of trying to forgive and accept the whole problem Lee should first accept something simpler: that someone did something bad. This moves the problem to the other person. It is not Lee's failure to deal with, but someone else's. In the other person's eyes they may not even feel they have done wrong, but that is a matter for their own conscience. Whether or not the other person will do anything to redress the matter (or even thinks that they should) is up to them.

The third thing to do seems very odd and Lee will really resist doing this at first; but it results in training Lee's brain to think completely differently about someone.

Propaganda is information delivered by an enemy that contradicts popular knowledge. It works by repeating the same message over and over until people simply accept it as true; whether it's verifiably true or not. Lee can use exactly this technique to modify their own opinion of someone that has caused them great harm or against whom they hold a great resentment.

Get Lee to write a short paragraph about this person. The paragraph should identify them by name and wish them happiness and all that their hearts might desire. Lee should read this out loud every a day for a month. Nobody needs to see them do this. They can do this alone and in private, but it should be done out loud because, as mentioned before, saying things out loud commits them more successfully into the mind.

It sounds an unlikely thing to do, but it works. At the end of the month Lee will be able to recall events involving this person without invoking any feeling of resentment towards them.

In the end it is forgiveness that is the path out of items on this list, but Lee won't like it. Forgiving people that have treated you badly is difficult, but tell Lee this: "You aren't forgiving them because *they* deserve forgiveness; you're forgiving them because *you* deserve peace". The motivation to do this is that Lee will feel better about the world; the other person actually receives nothing at all.

Things I have done that hurt someone else

The third group of issues to deal with are the occasions where Lee has done something that resulted in harm to others. These incidents if left as they are will remain with Lee forever. This part of the work brings these issues to closure with only a few exceptions.

Central to closing off these problems is meeting the person wronged and admitting the wrongdoing, but sometimes this shouldn't be done. If talking about the wrongdoing causes more harm to the person concerned then it should be left alone; Lee can't save their own skin at someone else's expense. Also, there are instances where discussing the issue is simply impossible, and there are those that would have a violent outcome if it was attempted. A means to close these will be discussed last.

Things that have ended badly and involved harm to others can be resolved completely, but this involves a very significant challenge for Lee. This process is extremely beneficial, but it is also very challenging. As with many other things to do with recovery from alcoholism, it is easy to say, but difficult to actually do. Lee will need your encouragement to complete this successfully.

For each issue Lee ideally needs to meet the wronged person face-to-face. The great advantage of a meeting in person is that much of how we communicate with each other is actually non-verbal. When we are in direct conversation with someone then both parties are constantly reading the expression and body language of the other to verify or otherwise the things that are being said. When we meet in person we don't just exchange information we exchange emotions that validate, reinforce or diminish what is said. It confirms sincerity. It isn't always possible to meet in person, and for those occasions Lee might call or write, but is not as effective as it lacks that exchange of emotions.

At the meeting Lee will identify what wrong they've done and make an unreserved apology for that. This is an apology that is made without implying that any part of the blame lies with the other party, and does not include any attempted justification or minimisation. Lee will find this challenging as there are always two sides to any argument, but Lee needs to keep firmly in mind that the apology is for what they have done, and *only* what they have done. What the other person did or didn't do is not a part of this conversation. The apology is to be immediately followed by this (or similar) phrase: "Is there anything I can do to put this right?" Lee is asking how they can make amends for what they did. It is this question, not the apology that leads Lee to being able to bring closure to the issue.

There are several ways the conversation can go at this point; some good and some bad, but all responses allow Lee a way to put the problem away permanently.

If the person says something that Lee should do by way of making amends, then Lee must do it. Once this is done then the matter is explicitly put right; the wrong is forgiven and the matter is ended. Even if restitution will take some time to achieve then the issue is on its way to resolution; progress is being made on the problem, and that is sufficient to give relief.

If the meeting goes very well then the wronged person might just dismiss the matter and say it's no longer a problem. Again, the wrong is forgiven.

If the meeting goes badly then the wronged person might get angry and say that they never want to see or hear from Lee ever again. This too brings closure. In this case Lee has been told that there is nothing left that can be done to change what's happened. It is what it is and a different resolution doesn't exist. There is therefore nothing left to be done.

These meetings are extremely challenging and Lee will need encouraging to do them, and to do them properly. If done properly each of these (there won't be too many that Lee needs to deal with) will be closed permanently.

After each of these "amends" Lee will need to spend a little time letting the matter rest before then accepting the state of the issue: there is nothing further to be done with it. It is time to accept it and put it away.

There are however some wrongs that cannot be raised in a face-to-face meeting; the consequences of the meeting or the conversation are simply too damaging for either one party or the other. Not all alcoholics have issues of this magnitude, but some do. For these issues (if they have any) Lee needs to decide their own amends; what is an appropriate restitution? This shouldn't be financial, but some sort of compensating service to the community. When Lee has completed that, then they should consider the damage repaid, and move on to accept that part of their past.

These individual acts of apologising and asking what must be done to put things right are extremely painful to complete. But once done they give Lee permanent relief from these parts of their past.

Acceptance

If Lee has verified that what that should be done to change things has been done, and that forgiveness and amends have been achieved where possible, then they must accept in turn each of their issues as they stand.

Lee needs to recognise that what's done is done; there's nothing further to be done to change them so continuing to think on them will yield no benefit. But this is far easier to say than to achieve and phrases like "get over it", "let it go" or "just move on" don't tell us *how* to accept these things, only that we should. Accepting things that we wish were different is not easy, but, there are things Lee can do that help them achieve this.

"Accept" is a verb; it is an active process not a passive one. If we can't change a situation we don't like, then we must change the way we think about it, or continue to suffer. The trick here is in finding the key that allows us to change the way we perceive the issue, and this takes deliberate thought. You can't talk to Lee about their secrets, but you can talk about acceptance, and this will help them enormously; the more issues Lee is able to bring to closure, the more the pains of their past are diminished.

If a particular issue cannot be changed then it must be "accepted" for it to cease to cause Lee distress. In this particular sense "accept" means: "To believe or come to recognize that a proposition is valid or correct".

The proposition is that an issue, or the outcome of an issue, can't be changed. I.e. it happened in the past and there's nothing to be done to change it, or it is happening now or in the future and is inevitable.

If this proposition is true, then there's no point whatsoever in thinking on it further. There's nothing that can be done to change it. Dwelling on this matter further will never achieve a different result, it will only bring anguish. It is time to stop thinking about it.

Get Lee to examine the issues in the lists one-by one. Encourage them to try to identify why this thing is hard to accept; this will narrow the possibilities and give them some focus on what it is they are trying to overcome. Another way to make acceptance easier is to list all the possible explanations for why they're still holding onto the event. Once Lee has done these then they might see if one or more of these ways of looking at the issue will allow them to set it aside.

- *Control.* We can only change issues that we can exert some control over. Is this event outside of Lee's sphere of control? If it is there there's nothing whatsoever to be done about it, and therefore thinking further on it will achieve nothing
- *Accept the fact that we will never know the answer to some questions.* If Lee is never going to know the answer then continued searching is fruitless and thinking further on it will achieve nothing
- *Life isn't fair.* Don't let Lee hold onto something from the past because it wasn't fair. Bad things happen. Bad things happen to everyone. Nobody has ever said that life was meant to be fair; life is not fair. The more Lee

can recognize that life is inherently not fair, the easier it will be to accept adversity and misfortune

- *We are not perfect.* Nobody knows everything, nobody is always right, and nobody goes through life without making mistakes. Lee does not have to have all the answers. It is OK to be wrong, and it is OK to make mistakes
- *Is this only a problem because of pride?* Is Lee too proud to accept an alternate interpretation? If so then pride is the issue, not this. Put this one away and work on diminishing pride and lifting humility
- *Other people are not perfect.* Just as we make mistakes, so do other people. Other people aren't perfect, and other people aren't always right and other people make mistakes. Try to get Lee to allow other people to have failings instead of requiring them to be perfect. Then Lee will be better able to accept their words and actions
- *Forgive yourself.* People are allowed to make mistakes. Lee is a person. Lee should try not to repeat the mistake in the future, but forgive themselves for the mistakes they make
- *Being 'in the right' will not fix this.* Believing that we are right achieves nothing whatsoever if the outcome is unsatisfactory; the event remains unchanged. In the same way being angry, remorseful, resentful, aggrieved

etc. also achieves nothing whatsoever. The event does not change; we are simply inflicting suffering on ourselves for no purpose by thinking about this in terms or right and wrong. Try to tell Lee to get off their high horse, stop complaining about it, and move on; everyone else has

- *Find the lesson.* Make the pain behind an issue meaningful. Sometimes the "worst" thing that happens to us ends up being an important part of our personal growth. Try to get Lee to accept the lesson, and having learned, move on
- *There is no choice except to accept.* This is a catch-all solution. If the other ways to look at the issue haven't helped then tell Lee there is no choice *but* to accept it, regardless of any reservations they may have. What's done is done. Let what has happened stay in the past. Learn from it, forgive it, release it, and work to live each day starting from a clean slate. Take the lesson they should from the past, but don't allow it to hold them back

Acceptance is achieved by looking at each issue in turn. This can't be done in one sitting and Lee will need to deal with only a very few each day. Get Lee to look very closely at the issue from all angles and ask: Is there something I should do to change this, or can't it be changed? There should by now be nothing further to change. If it can't be changed then look again. If there truly is nothing to change then it is what it is. It is finished with. Thinking further on it is simply wasting time and energy. Lee must put it down. When Lee can say of the matter "it is what it is" and feel no adverse emotional reaction, then it is accepted.

As Lee is able to accept more and more of the issues in their lists then their day-to-day mood will lift. Their past issues will cease to come back and haunt them. The memories are still there, but they are not constantly brought to Lee's attention and if they do they don't bring with them all the associated negative emotions. They will however re-surface periodically, summoned into consciousness through a link to something else that's occurred.

Lee has taken a list of issues from the past, and one by one brought them to a point of resolution. At this point the recurring problems should drop away, but occasionally they will come back stirred by related memories. When this happens Lee needs to press them back firmly. "I've done all the thinking I need to do about that, and the subject is closed". This issue has been fully examined and resolved, it is not necessary to think about it again, and Lee needs to instruct their brain that this is the case; out loud if possible. Once the issue is resolved then there is no value at all in rethinking it, and Lee needs to reject any call to do so.

A different future

The first part of this book looked at what alcoholism is, how it works in the brain and what to do to break the feedback loop of addiction. The second part looked at what could be done to clear up the wreckage of the past. This part looks at the future and is a complete step-change in the recovery process. The heavy lifting of recovery is done with and Lee next has to learn how to live a worthwhile life without alcohol, and this is important: it gives resilience to their sobriety.

If Lee goes through the whole process of breaking their addiction and fixing up their past but still doesn't enjoy life, then inevitably the question will come; is it worth it? The dominant memory about alcohol is that "drinking = fun". If they are still dissatisfied with life after all they've gone through then the idea of taking a drink will again become appealing. It will slowly nag until Lee yields to "Just one won't hurt!"

But there's also another trap. Lee is an alcoholic. This means that their brain has some deeply learned mental pathways that can never be un-remembered; in this respect Lee will remain an alcoholic (albeit a non-drinking one) for the rest of their life. They also have the deeply established memory that alcohol relieves distress and brings happiness. These memories linked to drinking never go away. But alcohol isn't the only issue.

Lee has the pre-requisite conditions for addiction; their brain significantly over-values the immediate benefits of certain things and does not recognise or significantly under-values any associated risk. Also they have a pre-disposition to take an immediate gain ahead of bigger, later benefits.

Lee is exposed to the risk of addiction for their whole life; not just alcohol, but all addiction. In the case of an alcoholic the possibility of forming a new addiction is high. The mental pathways of the addiction loop are still present: experience distress, and then relieve the distress with something that causes more distress. It is only a small sideways mental step for Lee's addiction to alcohol to transfer itself to a different substance or activity.

Lee needs to be made aware (it's likely they already sense this) that they are susceptible to addiction, and need to be forever cautious about what they expose themselves to. This isn't a difficult thing to do. If you know you're extremely likely to get hooked onto something, and you've already experienced the pain of escaping addiction, then it's fairly easy to back away and say "no" at the appropriate time. But Lee needs to be explicitly rather than vaguely aware of this vulnerability. But Lee has to be able to not only live without alcohol, they also have to get along without someone looking over them and guiding them at every turn. It is improved self-awareness that is central to a lasting recovery.

This part of the book looks at changes Lee can make in the way that they live that will reduce the likelihood of relapse, and avoid other addictions. It is about achieving and maintaining long-term recovery. The actions suggested here have nothing to do with drinking, rather they direct Lee towards living in a way that drinking adds nothing to their enjoyment of life; it is quite simply unnecessary.

Drinking impulses will be triggered for the rest of Lee's life. But these aren't the debilitating cravings endured during withdrawal, they are smaller, and as Lee's sobriety strengths they become more infrequent and easier to push back. It is this that often leads to a relapse after several months of abstinence, and Lee is very likely to meet it. After all the pain of withdrawal and the passage of time the amount of dopamine and stimulant in their brain normalises and finds a new equilibrium. The cravings that were originally continuous and insistent fall away and Lee may not even notice a craving for periods of days at a time.

The problem has changed

Lee no longer needs to stay on constant high alert ready to fight off a vicious call to drink. The cravings now occur seemingly "out of the blue" (though there's always a trigger for them) and are usually easy enough to fend off. Lee's sobriety is becoming more robust. They feel like they're back in control and this idea is going to pop into their mind. "Perhaps I'm cured". You need to warn Lee that this will come, and talk it through with them; they are not. Without exception, every single alcoholic who thought they might be cured discovered to their great discomfort that they were not.

Many fall to this temptation after a few months. The idea that they can now manage their drinking sets in, and in some jovial setting they decide to try "just one". The story of what happens next is completely consistent. "Just one" becomes "just one" the next day too, except this time it isn't one. The day after that it's several drinks, and very shortly after they're plunged right back into the depths of despair, drinking uncontrollably. It is a terrible sight to see when someone who has come so far is suddenly right back where they started from and can't understand how it happened. But *nobody* is cured of alcoholism. The automated processes that drove the addiction are still present and just like with a muscle, lack of use has made the processes weaker. But as soon as they are used again they very quickly regain their strength and the feedback loop reforms and takes over.

Alcoholics often attribute relapse like this to becoming complacent, but that isn't really what happens. They don't know how it happened because the automatic processes kicked in at a time when there was nothing there to oppose them. They respond automatically, driven by feelings rather than ideas. When they look at why they started to drink again they can see no reason, because there isn't one; no "reason" was ever formed. In the face of the lack of any explanation they say they became complacent. But the real issue is that the nature of the problem changed.

Lee is going to have to spend the rest of their life alcohol-free. But as time passes the memory of the depth of their suffering fades; what it was like as a drinking alcoholic, and what they went through while breaking the addiction cycle. These awful memories are slowly repressed and in time Lee won't even be able to accurately recall the depths of the emotional distress endured.

When Lee first stopped drinking then they had to spend every hour of every day on high alert; ready to fight off the huge cravings that would come. Over time the cravings stopped being big, and they stopped being regular. The challenge is now how to deal with a craving that suddenly jumps up "out of the blue", and the key to stepping past *that* craving is for Lee to constantly remind themselves that they are still an alcoholic. I.e. there is still a problem, and they still can't drink.

Lee needs a way to keep their handicap in mind even though their life seems to be no longer to be impacted by it, and this won't happen spontaneously, it needs deliberate prompting or it will slip away. The best advice you can give to Lee is that they need a marker in their day when they deliberately remind themselves of their true position. Lee needs a point in their daily routine when they tell themselves "I am an alcoholic". This alerts them to the fact that they still have a mental illness (even though it is dormant), that their illness needs treatment to be kept in remission, and that they can never safely drink again. The prompt "I am an alcoholic" is enough to set the brain working on the statement and keep it "front and centre".

Help them to find this moment. A likely time is as they are washing and getting ready for the day. Get them to put a reminder somewhere obvious for a while, like on the bathroom mirror for example. It should simply say "I am an alcoholic", and when they see it, Lee should say it out loud. This will set a routine going. You will need to check for a while that Lee is actually doing this but after a couple of weeks the mirror (or whatever is being used) will itself become a prompt for the action, and the message can be removed. As Lee uses the mirror in the morning "I am an alcoholic" will jump into their mind automatically.

If Lee can routinely link this idea to an everyday object then the central message of recovery can be sustained in their mind. It seems a trivial and almost silly thing to do, but if you can bring about delivery of this daily reminder then you are giving Lee a huge long-term defence against relapse.

The next thing you can do is help Lee make small changes in the way that they live that help make the feeling that they need a drink simply cease to occur.

Alcoholics have two particularly powerful triggers that induce the urge to drink: feeling unhappy or feeling dissatisfied with life and distressed. These bring back the memories that drinking is fun, and that drinking relieves distress. Lee has very real and powerful memories that re-inforce both these ideas and those memories never go away. But it is impossible to live in the world and always be happy and always feel relaxed; life has its ups and downs, and everybody is affected by them at some stage.

There are some simple things we can change in our lives that avoid us creating unnecessary mental discomfort, and some are listed here. None of the suggestions presented in this chapter relates to alcohol at all. These are not things Lee must do or avoid to stay sober; they are things that will lift Lee's day-to-day contentment so that cravings are triggered less often and when they come they are passed more easily. These ideas do not need to be pursued to perfection, or indeed at all, but it will make Lee's passage through recovery easier if they engage them.

You are not trying to turn Lee into an angel. It is not suggested that you try to get Lee to suddenly start doing these new things, rather that should the circumstance arise you take the opportunity to point out "you know you're just making things more difficult for yourself by..." The aim here is only to reduce the times Lee does some everyday things that unnecessarily detract from their enjoyment of life. The more content they are with life then the less they'll be challenged by cravings.

Stop trying to control the uncontrollable

Life is chaotic and unpredictable; things happen we don't expect and things happen we don't like. But this is the world as it is, and that's the reality of it. Planes, trains and buses run late. Traffic and road works obstruct our passage. We get delayed. People turn up late or appointments get cancelled. Shops and malls get busy, and sometimes you can't find what you're looking for. We misplace things, break things, and lose things. These and myriad more similar problems disturb what we want to achieve in our daily lives. But none of them lies within our control.

Things in our daily lives that interfere with what we want to happen can build a mounting level of distress and frustration; but we are powerless to change so many of them. When you see this happening you should remind Lee to accept what can't be changed and let it go. Stop. Breathe. Accept. Let it go. Move on. When things aren't going their way, then they should "go with the flow" of the world instead of kicking against it. If Plan A fails, then switch to Plan B, and if Plan B doesn't work then there are still 25 more letters to go. "Don't sweat the small stuff". Change what should be changed, and accept what can't.

Expectations

If we set our minds to expect things to happen certain ways then we are setting ourselves up for future disappointment. If we fantasise about the achievement of some plan or project then we are almost certainly pre-determining that we will be disappointed. Plans don't turn out as well as we wanted, they don't happen as fast as we wanted or maybe they don't happen at all. When we form expectations we make predictions about the future, but our ability to accurately predict the future is truly appalling. The world is unpredictable and there are countless reasons why plans and dreams don't happen as we visualise them.

Creation is motivating, but expectation is demanding. So, instead of expecting something to happen, or expecting a person to act a certain way, try to get Lee to focus on creating the pathway to achievement of some goal, but steer them away from daydreaming about the achievement of the goal itself. We can control a plan, and we can change a plan as we go along, but we can't necessarily control the achievement of a plan. So try to stop Lee from predicting the future, and discourage the formation of expectations.

Be honest

Sir Walter Scott said it well when he wrote "Oh what a tangled web we weave when first we practise to deceive". If we tell someone a lie then we must forever after avoid saying anything that will expose that lie, not only to that person, but also to anyone that they might communicate with. Telling lies is an enormously burdensome business and most often isn't worth the penalty. "Honesty is the best policy". It may be a little uncomfortable at the time, but it is usually far better to tell the truth of the matter (perhaps as gently as possible) rather than lie about it. If the truth will come out in the end, then lying serves no purpose whatsoever as deferring the discomfort of being honest does not avoid it, it makes it bigger. Occasionally it really *is* better to avoid telling the truth to someone rather than expose it; times when saying something to someone will cause them suffering and distress for example. But these occasions are rare, so Lee should find ways to tell the truth, or with each one they tell they will add another unnecessary burden... and they went to so much trouble to be rid of them!

Stop feeling entitled

The world does not owe Lee much, and it certainly does not owe them happiness. People are not queueing up to say how brilliant Lee is. People are not queueing up to lavish them with riches or power. The State may have some obligations to provide for them in some limited measure, but if they want more then that is up to them. The world isn't coming to Lee with solutions to their problems; they have to make them themselves.

Owning other people's problems

Lee is responsible for their own actions, not those of other people. It is Lee's job to live in ways that do not compromise their own conscience. What other people do is their problem, not Lee's.

Expecting life to be fair

Life isn't fair, it is unpredictable and chaotic. There is good and bad in the world, and there is good fortune and bad fortune. This is the way the world is and Lee should accept this, it's just how things are. Lee must accept what can't be changed, and do something about what can.

Allow yourself to be flawed

Lee does not have to always be right, and they do not have to have all the answers. It's OK to not know the answers to everything, it's OK to get things wrong, it's OK to make mistakes and it's OK to ask for help. Asking for help isn't weakness, asking for help is stating that we are in need, and that's a completely different thing. We are human; we are not perfect. So Lee should learn to accept their imperfections. Yes, try hard to improve, and learn from mistakes, but try to get Lee to step back from requiring constant perfection in everything they say, think and do.

Allow other people to be flawed

Not only are we not perfect, nobody else is either. People make mistakes. People have flaws, people have issues and they have problems. We do not know what drives other people, nor do we know the standards and values that guide them. What seems right and wrong to us may well be different for them. Lee needs to learn to allow other people the same latitude as they should give themselves; i.e. allow other people to not know all the answers, allow them to make mistakes, allow them to be less than perfect. If necessary Lee should allow them to be mentally unwell too... who is "normal" anyway?

Re-describe failure

Despite our best efforts and intentions things go wrong, but that's how we learn and grow. Experience is what you get just after you needed it. Try to get Lee to stop and deliberately look back over things when they go wrong and find the lessons in them. If Lee can change failure into education then they can move on, stronger and wiser for the experience instead of wallowing in self-loathing.

Be true to yourself

We are at ease with ourselves when we live within the bounds of our own conscience, not that of others. Try to encourage Lee to let go of trying to please others and seeking other people's praise. Lee should do what their own conscience says is right, not what someone else says, wants or expects; that's their values, not Lee's.

Self-honesty

Encourage Lee to be honest with themselves; scrupulously and brutally honest. If possible they should check themselves routinely and ask "how do I feel?" They should examine themselves based on how they actually feel about something, not on how they think they should feel, or how others might expect them to feel. It is how Lee actually feels themselves that determines their emotional response to an issue.

Being right for the sake of it

Not every argument is even worth having, let alone winning. More often than not an argument achieves nothing other than cause animosity; being right or winning the argument has no beneficial value whatsoever. Talk to Lee about avoiding arguments that will end with no positive outcome. Does winning this argument achieve anything? Is the world improved by being right on this matter? If it isn't then Lee should simply not engage, otherwise they're making someone dislike them for no benefit, and there is no point in needlessly turning people away from them. Does it need saying? Does it need saying now? Does it need saying by Lee?

Apologise

Try to get Lee into a practice of apologising *immediately* when they are wrong. This is a simple way of avoiding issues building up and becoming resentments that have to be put right later. The purpose of apologising immediately is that this is when an apology is both easiest to offer, and easiest to accept. If Lee delays an apology then the positions polarise. Lee will start to justify their own position, and resentment mounts in the other party. An apology that is offered immediately is easily accepted, and the matter closed before it even becomes significant.

Criticising people

One of the features of our subconscious mind that was identified earlier was that it "takes everything personally". When we judge people with a criticism then our brain responds emotionally as though that criticism was directed at us. The criticism doesn't need to be spoken, just thinking it is enough to trigger the emotional response. Calling someone an idiot raises in ourselves the emotion as though *we* have been called an idiot; indignation and anger follow. Try to get Lee to notice when they do this, and stop doing it. If Lee should have an insulting thought about someone then they can counter the negative emotion by immediately thing something positive about that person. It is a simple trick that stops us from bringing down our own day. Stop being critical of the things that people say, are and do.

Being important

Being important is rarely actually important, and striving to be seen as important is a fool's course. It is a sure way to make people dislike you. Don't let Lee talk themselves up, they should let their actions speak for them. We are what we do, not what we say we'll do, and that's how people actually measure us. The things we say we're going to do don't actually carry any significance at all until we do them.

Complaining

We make ourselves miserable when we moan about things. Simply repeating and repeating a problem does nothing to overcome it. Complaining about a problem re-affirms it and makes it persist, and with a persistent problem comes the frustration associated with it. If you find Lee bemoaning something then remind them that they should either do something to change the problem, or accept it; one or the other. They shouldn't sit on the fence moaning, it only keeps them frustrated with the world and is a very unattractive characteristic. Lee will feel better and people will like them more if they don't complain.

Do "should" before "want"

Encourage Lee to do the things that *should* be done before the things that they *want* to do. Doing them in the reverse order leaves tasks outstanding that nag while they remain undone. This is a simple way to have an easier and more satisfying day.

Life has enough problems in it without unnecessarily adding to the burden. None of the things listed above is essential to staying sober, but they will all help; the more content Lee is the less likely they are to be severely challenged by cravings, and the better prepared they are to meet them.

None of these items causes a major source of discomfort but collectively they are significant, and they are all stresses that are avoidable. Quite simply, life is easier without them. None of these is hard to do, and with a little perseverance they become habitual. They don't need applying all the time. Some of them will only be useful infrequently, and some may not be relevant to Lee at all.

You are not trying to turn Lee into an angel. The purpose of these is to improve Lee's general experience of life by removing pointless distress. Being content with life keeps them immune from "poor me!"

Self-image

The better Lee feels about themselves the less appeal alcohol has. If Lee is happy and content then there is simply no benefit in drinking alcohol, it adds nothing to their life; they are quite literally happy without it. But when Lee was still drinking they had an extremely poor self-image. They hated themselves. They were despicable, unlovable and worthless. Not much has happened to change that; drinking alcoholics have an incredibly poor self-image, and Lee is no exception. This must be changed if Lee is to avoid relapse. Lee can do some things that will make them feel better about themselves and their place in the world, and you can steer them towards doing the things that will improve their self-image.

Each of us responds emotionally to how good or bad we think we are, but unlike the speedometer of a car that shows us how fast we are going we have no direct gauge for the state of our self-image. We *feel* how well (or not) we are at any time, this is our prevailing mood, but we don't have a direct measurement of it.

We can't directly access the condition of our self-image, but we can estimate it by asking ourselves these four questions:

- How worthy do I think I am?
- How capable do I think I am?
- How loveable do I think I am?

– How valued do I think I am?

If Lee was asked to respond to these questions while they were still drinking they would give themselves extremely low scores on them all (perhaps with the exception of "capable").

How worthy we think we are is a reflection of how we feel in regard to our contribution to society. Humans evolved to live in groups, and the group's welfare was important to survival. For this reason our brain gives us a reward when we do something that aids the group but is not necessarily advantageous to ourselves. When we do something that benefits our community then we feel better within ourselves

How valued we think we are is our interpretation of the recognition we get from others. It is how often people thank us for what we do. If we don't do worthwhile things then nobody is ever going to say thank you and if we don't meet people then there's no possibility of people thanking us

How capable we think we are is also linked to our evolution to survive in groups. The more capable think we are, then the more we can contribute to the group's survival. This too results in a reward of a feeling of general wellbeing

Everybody has a basic need to feel wanted and accepted within our group, and *how loveable* we feel we are is our internal measure of this.

Once we understand what determines how we feel about ourselves, then we can set about deliberately changing it; talk to Lee about this. Describe the four main components of well-being and challenge Lee to come up with things they can do to improve them. Here are some suggestions.

Do things for other people

Of the things we can do that make us feel better about ourselves this one is the most potent and it is quite easy to achieve. When we do things that help others without expecting personal reward then our brains produce more of the drugs that make us feel that all is well in the world, and this effect is not short but enduring. If Lee can find some cause or activity that helps other people or the community then they will get a huge lift in their sense of wellbeing. Any activity at all that benefits others will do this, and you should do whatever you can to help Lee find a suitable cause.

The rewards from such an activity for a recovering alcoholic are enormous. Their sense of worthiness will lift and they form relationships in a new community that doesn't have drinking alcohol as one of its main reasons to exist. They socialise, and they do things that people may give people cause to say "thank you" (increasing how valued they think they are).

Re-join the world

Being outside of social communities deprives us of the opportunity to feel likeable or loveable. But recovering alcoholics are usually very shy socially. For most alcoholics the beginning of their addiction lies back in their early teens. They describe feeling somehow separate from their peers and not feeling like they fitted in.

One of the effects of alcohol on the brain is that it triggers the release of serotonin, the drug responsible for making us feel that we are socially significant. This is why when people drink they become self-confident and outgoing. If Lee felt this disconnection when they were young then alcohol made it possible for them to join in, to be a part of the group. It allowed them to feel self-assured among other people. In the following years Lee continued to use alcohol to be able to join in, and typically they would drink before social occasions.

Most alcoholics lack the social skills to feel confident among other people when sober. It's a skill they never acquired. Additionally, in the later stages of their addiction, they commonly withdraw socially and isolated themselves based on the idea that if their drinking was not seen then they wouldn't be shamed for it. This often develops into anxiety when being among unfamiliar people.

Now that Lee doesn't have alcohol to create that confidence they are anxious and even fearful of social engagement; they never learned how to do it. They doubt their ability to stand their own ground in social encounters, let alone shine... which was the sensation they had while drunk.

Lee may resist socialising; it makes them feel vulnerable. Ask them about this. Ask how they feel about attending social gatherings and try to identify just what the barriers are to Lee joining in, and what can be done to lower them. Overcoming this unwillingness to socialise is a major challenge for most alcoholics, but it must be overcome; if Lee doesn't socialise then the number of opportunities to improve how "lovable" and "valued" they think they are is severely reduced, and so is the capacity to enjoy life.

Learning to socialise again is difficult, most particularly because social occasions commonly have alcohol at them. One of the side benefits of AA or similar recovery groups is that there it is possible to meet and talk to new people. One of the reasons it's easier to talk to people there is because there's a natural subject matter for conversation. There are no uncomfortable silences.

If Lee is having difficulty socialising then you might deliberately look for occasions where conversation will be easy because there's a topic readily available. Lee might also look at joining one or more on-line recovery communities.

There are many of these, and Lee can participate in them without the anxiety of meeting people face-to-face.

You should encourage Lee as much as possible to do things build a new social life, one that does not revolve around bars, clubs and drinking. Occasions that involve some sort of activity are good as these allow Lee to meet new people but also have a subject matter to discuss. Try to encourage Lee to just say an immediate "yes" to invitations that are appropriate (i.e. not boozy parties). If they delay in responding then their fear may get the better of them and they will decline. But the truth is that once actually among company they will be fine and enjoy the occasion.

If alcohol is going to be present at an occasion then if at all possible Lee should not go unaccompanied at first; they may need the support if things get difficult. Simply having someone beside them that expects that they won't drink is very likely all that's required. But under all circumstances the most important thing is that Lee must have a way to leave if they need to.

Becoming sociable again is essential to Lee's long-term recovery. Time spent alone in their own head is the surest way to corrode away all the good work they've done in becoming well, so moving away from wanting to isolate is a good defence against this. But the other major benefit from being more social is that if Lee's life will begin to expand again.

Learn something new

Learning something new boosts how capable we think we are and that makes us feel better about ourselves. It's that simple. It doesn't matter what this new capability is; a skill, a craft, a language, a qualification... anything. They all serve the same purpose; to lift Lee's self-image. It is a simple and direct way to boost how capable they think they are. If Lee can find something new to master early on in their sobriety it will also help fill those times when they need their mind occupying.

Working on maintaining and improving their self-image is a big tool for Lee in terms of their long-term recovery and overall wellness. Ask Lee periodically how they are scoring on the four questions: how loveable, capable, valued and worthy they think they are. This will direct them towards what they need to change to stay feeling content with their place in the world, and this keeps away any need for alcohol.

Staying well

Staying well requires maintenance of the things that got, and that keep Lee well. Alcoholism is a chronic illness. As long as it is being treated then its symptoms will be held at bay. But if the treatment stops, then the symptoms will return. To sustain sobriety requires that Lee develops a habit of checking themselves emotionally to see if they are as they should be in the prevailing circumstance. It is very easy to overlook a slow decline in wellbeing, most especially after a stretch of feeling well. But Lee is not the only person that can tell if things aren't quite right; you will see it too. You will see this as Lee withdrawing slightly, and becoming slightly unhappy and distant. When you see this you need to challenge Lee to check themselves: Have they stopped doing one of the things they should be doing? Have they started doing something they shouldn't be doing? Are there new resentments or recurring thoughts that are disturbing them? Are there things that should be accepted, or some things that need attending to?

Lee has the remedies for all of these, but needs to know when they should apply them. If they don't recognise the need to do something themselves, then some prompting won't hurt.

Of all the ways of maintaining a long lasting sobriety, the most effective is staying in contact with a supportive abstinence group. For most people AA will be the most accessible, but there are others. Someone that regularly attends 12-step (or similar) meetings is twice as likely to remain abstinent over a prolonged period as someone who doesn't. Regular attendance of 12-step or other recovery meetings reinforces the abstinence message. It holds the attendee accountable in front of their peers and it prevents backwards slippage.

Be grateful

Many therapies encourage "an attitude of gratitude" and this is the power of positive thinking in action. Patients are encouraged to list things that they're grateful for, but sometimes in this entitled world we live in it doesn't seem to offer much by way of a lift. It's difficult to feel grateful for a roof over your head and food to eat if that's already your legal right. Encourage Lee to write a list, or think about things they are grateful to *not* have since they stopped drinking. For example:

- Not feeling like death warmed up every morning
- Not feeling like their life's going backwards
- Not worried sick about what they might have done last night but can't remember
- Not coming to in the shower and wincing as awful memories of last night come creeping back
- Not trying to hide shaking hands

- Not wondering how they're going to explain themselves to friends, family and colleagues
- Not wasting most of their time, energy and money on drink
- Not losing friends and not making new enemies
- Not making a fool of themselves
- Not letting people down
- Not failing to keep promises

A list like this does not go out of date or change from day-to-day. If Lee can make a list of the bad things that they've made disappear by not drinking then this will give them a solid and enduring gratitude with respect to being alcohol-free. If they are wavering then get Lee to reread this list as a reminder of the benefits they have won so far by not drinking.

Relapse

Relapse is not to be feared, it is an essential part of stopping drinking.

It is not inevitable that Lee will relapse in the time you are helping them, but it is quite likely. If Lee sets out to stay sober but then drinks they will be utterly devastated and at a complete loss to understand why they can't manage such a simple thing.

Along the path there will appear to be setbacks like this. These are not failings on your part; the battle isn't one of logic, but of feelings. They don't happen because you have failed to transmit certain messages convincingly. They happen because the addiction is fighting back. If Lee picks up drinking again it is because their brain is demanding alcohol and trying all means to acquire it. As Lee closes the doors to alcohol one-by-one, their addiction searches for the ones that are still open. One was found. Lee is aware of it now and can close that one too. Stopping drinking is difficult, and just like other difficult things it takes time to master. We become proficient at doing things with practice, and we advance the most on the back of mistakes. This is how we learn.

The first failures Lee will have experienced are failures to limit the amount they drank. The intention would have been to "just have a couple"; but that's not how it would end. Following those there would be attempts to stop for a while, but these would collapse within a few days; some people manage longer, but not many. When Lee finally started to recognise the severity of their condition then there would have been more serious attempts at stopping; all ending at a bottle. All of these are relapses; occasions when the intention to not drink was not met. Recovery is a progression of learning steps.

Stopping drinking is hard and nobody really understands quite how hard it is until they try, and until they realise just how hard it is they don't bring enough to the attempt. But relapse isn't really *failure*, it is education. It is an essential step on the path to recovery. It is only through successive failures that alcoholics finally learn how to break the addiction cycle and then to remain alcohol-free.

Relapse isn't failure, it is growth. But this isn't how it will feel to Lee. To Lee it will be utterly devastating. They only had to do one simple thing, something that most other people can do easily, but they couldn't. Drinking again wasn't intended. It was not what was meant to happen, but it still did. Lee can't articulate the problem, because the problem didn't come in words it came as feelings, and on this occasion Lee was unable to get past them.

For Lee the position feels more hopeless than ever. Their earlier sense of impending doom and hopelessness is back in full force, deepened by the new evidence that for them it is impossible to stop drinking. They feel utterly useless, and have not only failed themselves, but they have failed everyone else too. They are at their wits end and in total despair; there is no escaping alcohol.

Lee desperately needs your help now. You need to stand them back up and get ready to give it another try.

The first thing to do is to crush the idea that relapse is failure.

Lee is trying to beat feelings with logic and reason, but feelings are untouched by persuasion. Carefully constructed arguments are only effective in lifting resolve, they do not diminish cravings. Lee hit a moment when the craving was high, but resolve was low, and in that moment feelings overpowered reason. This is what has happened. It was not weakness.

Lee's drinking again has not changed the problem. They are still alcoholic. They still can't limit or control their drinking. Alcoholism is still progressive, and uninterrupted will result in premature death. Continued drinking will drive them deeper into despair in a fatal downward spiral. It *is* still possible to stop drinking, lots of people do it.

What *has* changed though is Lee's understanding of the scale of the challenge; it is harder than they thought. Talk about this for a while, and re-visit the main points:

The goal is to become well, and enjoy a life free of the shame, guilt, loneliness, and misery that alcohol brought

Most people *do* recover

You don't need to have some super-power to stop drinking; ordinary people do it. Lee isn't lacking in some special quality that's needed to do it

Nobody, absolutely nobody is able to completely stop drinking at the first attempt; it is always preceded by relapse in one form or another

Nothing is lost; rather Lee has gained a deeper understanding of the challenge. Not only is nothing lost, they are not back at the beginning again. They are well advanced along the path, and only need to resume their progress. The good days while they stopped drinking are still good days, and the bad days when they did drink were important lessons. Both the good days and the bad days were experiences to draw strength from. Lee knows what it takes to go a whole day without drinking. They have done it multiple times, so they know they can do it. The bad days exposed more of the pitfalls, problems and triggers involved in getting sober. They also showed Lee that they are not cured, and they still can't control their drinking. Finally, Lee has been reminded that drinking brings misery and loneliness.

The problem has not got bigger, but Lee's ability to confront it has.

Stopping drinking is a huge obstacle to overcome and most will falter one or more times, and that's OK. At each stumble more is learned. You don't just get one attempt at recovery, and nobody says that you have to be successful at the first attempt; Lee can have as many tries as are needed.

Try to get Lee to talk about their drinking experience during this relapse. Lee's brain tells them that drinking is fun; that's the promise associated with alcohol. Was it true? Lee can use this experience to confirm to themselves that their brain tells them lies about alcohol. Alcohol is supposed to make them feel better, but now they feel worse than ever. Their circumstances haven't changed. All that happened to bring about this return to suffering is that they drank. Encourage Lee to write themselves a note and carry it with them. What is the advice they'd like to have received just before they picked up a drink?

Lee needs to understand that relapse is a part of the process, not the end of it. They aren't back at the start. They are in the middle, have paused, and now it's time to move forward again.

When Lee feels able to have another go then spend some time with them to take stock of their position and review the help that they'd engaged; perhaps it is time to broaden this. Did they visit their doctor? Did they get medication to support them through withdrawal? Did they talk to anyone that had recovered? Did they participate in some regular recovery group meetings? What about other treatment options; should they be considered now?

When Lee's spirit has been lifted again you need to spur them back into action with a message of hope. "Off you go again then. You've had a rest, now it's time to carry on. It's hard, but it's worth it. You're not giving up the only thing that's good; you're giving away something that's destroying you. You know how to do this better now. You're stronger now. Sobriety delivers all the things that alcohol promised. You've got it this time."

It's not your problem

This book has laid out the practical things that you can do to help Lee recover from alcoholism, but what if they're not open to being helped?

The starting point for any recovery is accepting that alcohol is causing a problem and that something needs to be done about it. It is a completely pivotal point. Until Lee accepts that their drinking is a problem then there's nothing at all that can be done to help them. Until they can see that there's a problem then they have no need of a solution. Lee will continue to drink until this tipping point is reached, and bad things will continue to happen to Lee and those around them.

Lee is ill and has a huge problem to turn around, but if they are unwilling or unable to attempt that then you don't have to continue to share the burden of their problem. Lee is doing downhill, but doesn't have the right to take you with them. It is Lee's problem and it is up to Lee to fix it; nobody else can help them do that if they won't cooperate.

There are many things you can do to help Lee reach the point where they recognise that the pain of continuing exceeds the pain of stopping, but ultimately this is a conclusion that only Lee can reach, and you can't control the timing of that. It may be that Lee has to go further down before that tipping point is reached. But until then the chaos and damage continues.

Maybe Lee's time is yet to come, but you don't have to sit and endure the carnage until that day arrives. If you need to walk away for your own well-being and/or the wellbeing of others then that's what you must do.

Lee may in time reach the point that change becomes possible; most alcoholics get there sooner or later. Your action may indeed be the trigger that spurs this change, but you can't rely on that at all, and you can't make your decisions based on expecting this outcome.

You are not responsible for Lee's illness and you are not responsible for their recovery, only they can be that. But you are responsible for your own wellbeing, and you must take whatever action is needed to secure that.

Do not feel guilt or shame if you have to walk away. There may be a time you can go back, but until Lee is ready to change then there's nothing more you can do for them; look after yourself.

Hope is real

A drinking alcoholic is trapped into a state of complete hopelessness and they can see no way out of their trap. They are miserable and they are doomed. But they don't have to stay that way. Just because they can't see any means of escape doesn't mean that there isn't one; there is.

You can change everything for Lee, and that journey starts with hope. The loss of hope is what traps Lee in their despair; they can see no way out. But you can show them the way out. You can show them that their position is not hopeless at all, that recovery is indeed possible. You can show them why they think they're trapped, but also that millions of others have been there, that they have escaped it, and that Lee can too.

You can show Lee why they should break the grip of addiction, how to do it, and you can help them through breaking out of the feedback loop of addiction. You can show them how to be free of the horrors of their past, and you can show them how to live a simple and less troubling life.

Stopping drinking is not easy; nobody says it is easy. What recovered alcoholics say is that it is possible, and it is worthwhile. Most alcoholics do recover, and when they do they report having a completely new outlook on life. They describe a sense of contentment with their place in the world, and that gives them a previously unknown freedom and happiness. In comparison to the helpless torment that Lee once suffered, these are priceless beyond compare. When the weight of shame, guilt, fear and loneliness is lifted then Lee will feel in their place a deep calmness that they've never known before. This is the great prize of sobriety, and you can help them win it.

When you build hope in Lee then you re-shape their future, because recovery becomes possible when they stop seeing their position as hopeless.

Lee doesn't need to possess some magical superpower to stop drinking. They don't have to be the smartest person in the district to be able to stop, and they don't have to be the strongest, tallest, or fastest. What's needed to recover from alcoholism is hope, and you can give Lee that hope. On that foundation you can build willingness, and with willingness everything becomes possible.

Hope is not only real, it is infectious. Emotions are transmitted from one person to the other. The hope that you hold will be recognised by Lee, and in time they will come to believe it too. Your hope is Lee's hope.

Bless you for doing this.

Also by Stan West

How to help your alcoholic

If you have a partner, spouse, family member or close friend whose drinking is causing problems then they need help. They need help because they can't help themselves.

It *is* possible to help someone overcome a major drinking problem, and this book shows you how to set about it.

Understanding and learning from relapse

Relapse isn't failure, it is education. It is an essential step on the path to recovery. It is only through successive failures that we finally learn how to overcome the addiction and then how to remain alcohol-free. Relapse is not the end of a recovery effort; it is another step that advances us along the road to recovery. This book looks at relapse; what leads to it, how to overcome it, and how to use it as another learning step towards breaking free from addiction.

CPSIA information can be obtained
at www.ICGtesting.com
Printed in the USA
LVHW081023200122
708979LV00013B/216